THE KISSING GATE

Don Llewellyn

'Oft, in the stilly night,
Ere Slumber's chain has bound me,
Fond Memory brings the light
Of other days around me;
The smiles, the tears,
Of boyhood's years,
The words of love then spoken;
The eyes that shone,
Now dimm'd and gone,
The cheerful hearts now broken!'

Thomas Moore (1779-1852)

CYHOEDDWYR
DINEFWR
PUBLISHERS

Copyright © 2009 Don Llewellyn

Published in 2009 by
Dinefwr Publishers
Rawlings Road, Llandybie
Carmarthenshire, SA18 3YD

The right of Don Llewellyn to be identified as the Author
of the Work has been asserted by him in accordance with the
Copyright, Designs and Patents Act 1988.

ISBN 978-1-904323-16-7

A CIP catalogue record for this book is
available from the British Library.

Printed and bound in Wales by
Dinefwr Press Ltd.
Rawlings Road, Llandybie
Carmarthenshire, SA18 3YD

For Avril

Acknowledgements

The author thanks all those who read the first draft of the book for their encouragement and Mr Brian E. Wood for his meticulous proof-reading of the original manuscript.

Chapter One

The sweet song of a blackbird floated in through the open window. I turned my head and looked out to contemplate the cloudless blue sky, wishing I was outside, *doing* something – anything, rather than be sitting at a desk in a school that I didn't much care for anyway.

'Llewellyn! That blackbird will probably be singing after four o'clock. But the black *board* is over here, not by the window!' I faced front to see Eaglebeak smirking as he tapped the side of his leg with the cane that rarely left his hand. Of course, I'd been daydreaming again; but our headmaster, once described by my father as 'The Local Education Prevention Officer' was always pulling me up for something or other. Dad had meant no serious malice, and the two men would eventually come to respect each other. However, although *I* could never be sure about him, my friend Walter, master of the mischievous quip, remained unwavering in his opinion of the formidable-looking, hawk-nosed William 'Eaglebeak' David, referring to him as a 'waste of precious food'.

Like most, I have a mixed bag of memories. Some still hurt, but I also recall those long-gone lovely days that even now can fade in like a smile to remind me of the untrammelled joys of childhood. Albeit over the last sixty years hindsight has inevitably been coloured by the evolution of an adult perspective, my basic feelings haven't changed one jot since those distant days. As I was then, so I am now – a child at heart. Walter was right all those years ago when he called me a sentimental sod.

As the headmaster rose to address Assembly I could tell from his expression that he had something important to say. Always in a state of preparedness for an announcement that hordes of Germans had landed on our shores, we feared the worst. It was then that Eaglebeak seemed to relax somewhat to tell us of an altogether different invasion that was imminent.

The busload of evacuees was due at five o'clock and by 4.30 the grass bank at the Twyn was swarming with villagers. The air buzzed with an excited chatter of Welsh and English.

'Cocky knees from London, they'll be,' said Idwal Thomas with all the authority of a quarter-wit. 'My uncle told me that's what they're called.'

'I can't wait to get my 'ands on the buggers,' said Dilwyn Price-Davies, whose face bore the typically vacuous look of a bully.

My brother Gareth stood silent and still, confident in his strength and his sense of duty, his scout uniform – pressed to perfection by Mam – complementing the rather military bearing he'd lately adopted. Walter and I scurried about, stopping only to practice our newly-learned handstands in readiness for showing off to the new arrivals; that is, if they were to turn up at all. Nearly two hours later we were still there, with our reserves of patience dwindling.

The Twyn put me in mind of a gigantic anthill. A natural mound of about a third of an acre, it rose in an almost perfect curve to about twenty feet above the road. Opposite was one of the local pubs, correctly The Lewis Arms, but also known to everyone as the Twyn, taking its name from a spot revered by poets who found inspiration there and bruisers – who settled scores with each other. This evening, as the midsummer sun was setting over the distant edge of the Vale of Glamorgan, the hallowed patch pulsated with moving beings charged up by their native reluctance to miss out on any event worth talking about. Even the arrival of a new family in the village brought a degree of excitement to our lives; the prospect of dozens of new residents being suddenly thrust into our midst was exhilarating.

The rocky limestone outcrops that littered the mound like worn-down teeth provided natural seating for clustering families now showing signs of tiredness from waiting and trying to curb the scampering of excited children. Old Shinco Price, a veteran of the South African War, was left-handedly stabbing at passing juveniles with his walking stick, doubtless dreaming of Boers and bayonets. He would certainly have used his right hand had he not lost the arm at Mafeking.

My own mother had charged my brother with the responsibility of ensuring that I didn't stay out too late. For that reason I tried my best with Walter's help to keep out of his sight; even the immature can sense the need to watch history being made. I was safe for the time being, for Gareth was teaching a group of boys of his age how to tie complex knots in a length of string that had previously been holding up Dilwyn's trousers. The bully had been persuaded by my brother to part with it for the demonstration, unaware that it was Gareth's way of temporarily disarming the brute. Dilwyn often seemed to be simmering with suppressed rage and it usually took a superior mind like Gareth's to keep the peace. I felt quite proud as Walter and I went by on our knees through the long grass on the perimeter of the Twyn, only yards away from the group.

'I wish I 'ad a brother like yew do 'ave,' whispered Walter, when we were nearly out of earshot of the older gang. ''E's so bloody *clever*.'

'Aye,' I said.

I really wanted to shout to the world: 'Yes, my brother is a hero. He's brainier than anybody else in the universe and he's kind and he's strong and he swims like Tarzan and plays rugby and cricket for the grammar school and he can do equations and write essays about Julius Caesar and he knows the capital city of every country in the world and when he grows up he's going to be a barrister or a train-driver or a doctor or a manager at the quarry or an explorer in Africa. But if he catches me now and tries to take me home I shall kick him.' Nothing was going to stop me being present for 'The Important Event'.

We crawled to the side of the Twyn that faced the approach road, daring to stand up only when we were beyond any possible sighting by my brother. Back among the younger sages we sat down and listened to the idle chattering of wise nine-year-olds past their bed-time:

'They won't come now, it's too late.'

'Give 'em a chance, it's a long way from bloody London.'

'My uncle says they do think we all live in caves.'

'Will they have soddin' teachers with 'em?'

'An' will we understand 'em when they talk?'

'P'raps they were bombed an' they're all bloody dead.'

'No, mun. Don't worry, they'll be 'ere.'

A clutch of giggling girls and a gang of older boys moved up front, led by Idwal, a sturdy young man of twelve who towered above Walter and me.

'Comin' by train to Cardiff it is, they are, see,' said know-all Idwal, who never shunned an opportunity to experiment with English grammar. 'Then by bus to by 'ere, innit.'

There had been some false alarms. *'Heisht!'* someone would shout, commanding the crowd to instant silence as ears were cocked towards the point where the main road entered the village.

Another *'Heisht!'* and I felt my heart quicken as hopes were raised by the sounds of motors in the distance. We were deceived again as a small convoy of army lorries eventually approached and passed, making their way from Cardiff to the searchlight and anti-aircraft gun-site perched on the top of our mountain ridge. Most of us stood to attention and saluted as they went by; however, Walter ran after the last vehicle and tried to hang onto the tailboard. A small thirteen-year-old, Walter, who spent most of his time with those who were a couple of years his junior, was driven by an irresistible urge to jape.

My admiration for Walter Hopkins had grown from when I began to realise that the alleged dunce with the funny leg and vowels was always one step ahead of most of us. I refused to call him 'Hoppy' as others did, for I was never sure whether it was because of his surname or because he had one leg shorter than the other, giving him an odd limp. He was brighter and braver than most of my friends and although he could soak up insults like a sponge, he was no pushover in an argument. It certainly wasn't want of courage that made Walter drop off the back of the lorry so much as the rifle-butt that appeared mysteriously from behind a canvas flap, threatening to make mincemeat of his hands.

'Bloody Belgians,' said Walter, who had fallen heavily and bruised his shoulder. 'They were aimin' for my 'ead!' he said, with a rueful grin. He was the only one I ever knew who could smile at pain. His recovery was usually rapid and he would refuse all aid from the elders who might have fussed around him. Walter reckoned being kissed by 'aunties' was a fate even worse than running into Dilwyn in a narrow lane at night.

Calm returned and was only momentarily pierced by Bleddyn Morgan's horse and gambo going by with an early crop of hay. The old man was giving his animal a most complex series of shouted instructions in Welsh. It was a pointless exercise on two counts: firstly the horse had been brought up in Anglicized Cardiff, and secondly it was stone deaf.

At last a shrill call from Mervyn Joseph, whom Dilwyn had ordered up a tree as a lookout, indicated that a bus was approaching. He might have been apprising Nelson of the appearance of a French ship on the horizon, such was the seriousness of his announcement. Perhaps though, like most of us, he was simply terrified of Dilwyn.

'I can see the bugger, Dil!' screamed Mervyn, 'Red bus, it is, Dil . . . Out of it there's smoke comin'. There's bloody wonderful! It might blow up! First to see it, wasn't I, Dil? Me it was, Dil, who saw it first, isn't it?'

Soon the single-decker bus came into our view, grumbling its way up the last stretch of hill. The front end was engulfed in a steamy cloud through which we could just perceive the driver who was mouthing imprecations doubtless worthy of any local horse-beater. On reaching comparatively level ground, the rusty old thing stuttered for a few more yards, snorted like one of Uncle Gwilym's sows, and stopped with a jerk at the foot of the Twyn mound. That was when we first saw the faces, some bemused, some clearly worried, pressed against the steamy windows. For a few moments there was neither movement nor sound from the bus, except for the watery hiss from its nose.

By now our crowd had been swollen by the arrival of a couple of dozen more villagers, mostly women wearing Welsh shawls and a few with Welsh tears in their eyes. They were obviously going to enjoy having a bit of a sob.

I feared that despite our patience we wouldn't get a close view of the vital first moments of the visitors' emergence from the coach, for we were contained at the back of the throng, both by the crush of bodies and by my concern to evade my brother. But I'd reckoned without Walter, who was now fully recovered from his fall and ready for anything. I felt a sudden grip on my wrist as he pulled me headlong and low through a maze of legs and walking-sticks, past assorted bicycles and pramwheels until we came to a stop at the front, among a gang of councillors, local schoolteachers, and sundry chapel deacons.

As we settled at the kerbside the driver emerged from the bus with a grubby piece of paper that he handed to one of the welcoming group who had stepped forward.

'They're all yours now, Skip,' he grunted in a rich Cardiff accent. 'I think they're all deaf and bloody dumb! They haven't so much as whimpered all the way from Kairdiff General!'

The driver was approached by George Rogers, a veteran of the First World War, clad in the uniform of the Local Defence Volunteers and sporting his 1914-18 campaign ribbons. He saluted the incredulous driver before taking the piece of paper which he duly signed and returned. Said the one-time sergeant-major: 'You took your time didn't you?' Then, with a smile, 'Now bugger off back to Cardiff and be a bit quicker with the next lot!'

Returning to the bus, the driver managed a Parthian shot: 'Well they did warn me,' he shouted, pretending to spit to the ground, 'they're all bloody nuts up 'ere!'

The caged kids seemed reluctant to come out, despite the waves and smiles of the women whom they could just see through the misted windows. But Walter and I thought we knew what was really troubling them: a fist-shaking fourteen-year-old standing on top of the Twyn mound, silhouetted against the late evening sky. Dilwyn had a knack of ruining happiness; or so it seemed to Walter and me, for we had both felt the bully's senseless anger more times than we wished to remember.

It was the vicar who, with the confidence of his calling, decided to assume leadership of the welcoming host. He stepped into the bus and said something that would remain a mystery. Perhaps it was some of the mumbo-jumbo in which, my father always claimed, the vicar excelled. Whatever it was, it succeeded.

Thirty children aged between five and fourteen filed past us, some tearful, and others, I was glad to see, wearing broad smiles.

Most had few possessions apart from a label bearing their name, and a cardboard box containing the obligatory gas mask. Some though, carried toys: a plump boy wearing a Kent County Cricket cap struggled with a bundle of wickets; two or three had footballs and the last of the line, a sturdy fourteen-year-old, proudly sported two pairs of shiny red boxing gloves laced around his neck. We were clearly in for a very sporting time. Several girls clutched dolls that were in varying states of health. An extremely pretty girl of about my own age opened a cardboard box and proudly showed the attentive onlookers a tortoise.

There was more hugging going on than I had ever seen in a local derby rugby match. The atmosphere was redolent of lavender from shawls and vibrant with the warmth of ladies who knew how to love. The women of Pengarth were very special – almost every one was a *bopa*, a kind 'aunty'.

The vicar, the Reverend Islwyn Theophilus Bendigeidfran Jones BA, BD, had taken up position on the high ground to deliver his speech of welcome; his 'sermon on the mount' as my brother later described it.

'I cannot begin to fathom,' bellowed the Reverend Jones in the imposing tones and affected vowels which were trademarks of robed priests, 'how can authorities in their wisdom send such lovely young people from their wilderness to this haven without the accompaniment of mature and responsible care-takers? It is not even certain that they have come to the right place, but they may be assured,' he said, turning his gaze to the pathetic band of waifs, 'that they will be cared for here as if they were veritably the Children of Israel.'

Competition in public speaking had long been zealously pursued in the village and the vicar was not going to let this opportunity pass without milking it dry. He was aware of the presence of at least three nonconformist pastors who, given the chance, would have preached until dawn. Credit must be given to one of the village drunkards, who had wobbled out of the pub doorway, for getting things moving in the right direction. The swaying figure, trying rather unsuccessfully not to spill the contents of a pint mug of best Ely Ale, called out in Welsh: 'In the name of the great Redeemer, get those hungry and frightened young people indoors!' Following up in English: 'You miserable hypocrites!' Occasionally my father could be very embarrassing. Walter nodded towards the nearby chapel building and pulled me towards it.

The vestry of Horeb Welsh Calvinistic Methodist chapel stood on the other side of the Twyn from the Lewis Arms. It had been hurriedly designated as the assembly point for the evacuees, and Walter, with bright anticipation, had decided that we would need to quickly slip inside if we were to have a close view of the goings-on.

After we'd eased our way in through the wash-house window, conveniently unlocked earlier by Walter, we became aware of intense activity in the vestry. Village women, some wearing the uniforms of voluntary services, busied themselves setting trestled tables with bright linen cloths as an endless train of Welshcake-and-sandwich-laden trays made its way from a score of houses in the neighbourhood. I saw Bopa Martha come in with two big earthenware jars of nettle beer. Another bopa, Meia Jenkins, brought a big rhubarb pie from which a heavenly vapour emanated. Slabs of fruitcake were uncovered alongside loaves of freshly-baked bread, the warmth of which was felt by Walter and me as we crouched our way past, trying to remain undetected. Mrs Protheroe of Nant yr Arian farm entered proudly with a block of her famous butter. At the far end of the hall there was a cast-iron range on which immense kettles were singing to each other, their lids tapping merrily. Row upon row of cups and saucers sat on a nearby table waiting to be serviced by big brown teapots.

We managed to secrete ourselves in the corner of the hall by the Bible- store, half hidden by the ancient harmonium which I knew had played its triumphal part in the saving of souls since my great-grandfather's day.

All heads suddenly turned towards the heavy old vestry door as it creaked open to admit a Red Cross lady leading in the weary, dishevelled group. Escapees from the war over south-east England, they now seemed almost as terrified by the strange new world into which they had been flung. Many of the village people were speaking a language of which the visitors understood not a single word. The religious posters were undecipherable, as were the captions below several portraits of past giants of the Welsh pulpit and Liberal politicians, all looking sternly down.

At first timidly, then suddenly and with much enthusiasm, the 'Children of Israel' accepted the manna on offer. As their bodies warmed to the food, so their fears evaporated. Soon some were skipping and dancing with delight, and no chapel deacon present could reasonably remonstrate with them for profaning the House of God. One little girl took a plateful of food and proceeded to feed her teddy bear. A boy tugged at a lady helper's apron and asked if he could have another 'Welshy-cake'.

Walter and I were about to collapse with hunger and envy when we saw feet approaching our hiding place. We looked up to see a very pretty girl, the memory of whose face I had been unable to erase since that moment on the mound when she had shown off her tortoise. She handed us two plates of food.

'I could see you hiding,' she whispered. 'Thought you might be hungry.' She put a lovely face close to ours and said: 'Don't worry, there'll be no bombs tonight.' Then she waltzed back to her friends.

Walter and I consumed *our* heavenly bounty without any excited reference to its donor. Then we heard a call to attention.

The next step was to be the allocation of the children to their new homes.

An attempt was made to keep families together, but it wasn't always possible. We could see pain in the faces of separated siblings.

Certainly, neither Walter's home nor mine would be taking anyone, for our houses were too small. We both yearned for the rules to be broken and hoped we would hear that 'So-and-So' would be placed with the Hopkins family, and that 'Such-and-Such' would go to join the Llewellyns. Walter would want the boy with the boxing gloves and I knew he'd see him as a bodyguard to defend him against Dilwyn. One snap of Walter's fingers and out of the shadows would come his personal minder to batter the bully into oblivion . . .

My fantasy was the lad with the cricket stumps. We would play for hours on Clawdd Siôn field, with our new friend bowling, my brother batting, and me the ubiquitous fielder. I would run and run before returning the ball with deadly accuracy to our new friend at the bowling end. Then we would go home and talk ourselves to sleep telling each other lies about magnificent acts of heroism we had performed in our long and eventful lives. But even my dreams couldn't accommodate the real object of my longing; and, anyway, it was unlikely that my parents would like a girl *and* a tortoise in the house.

'Martin Greaves, you go with the nice Mrs Roberts of Temperance Row.'

'Susannah Gainsborough. Go to Morfudd Davies of Cefn Bychan.'

'Brian and Peter Lawton. Mr and Mrs Lloyd of Cwm Coed y Garth will look after you.'

'Mrs Angharad Davies, a fyddech mor garedig i edrych ar ôl y plentyn bach annwyl Katie Archer? Please look after Katie, Mrs Davies. I think it was your fruit cake that did the trick.'

17

One after the other the fears of the early evening subsided as infants were held to bosoms and older boys were handshaken and led away in manly fashion. Walter tried to persuade me to help him appropriate some of the remaining food, but I was transfixed by the sight of our pretty girl being handed over to Mrs Protheroe of Nant yr Arian farm. I watched as she calmly and serenely walked away with her new guardian and heard her ask Mrs Protheroe if she would like to see her tortoise.

That was the moment when Gareth rushed in and grabbed me by the collar to march me home. It was half past nine and I had rarely been out so late.

'Mam is hopping mad,' said my brother sternly, and with a sideways glance at Walter who had limped out with us, added: 'Sorry, Walter, no offence.'

Walter hopped away with a 'See yew tomorrow, Geraint.'

Our village of Pengarth stood on the slopes of a mountain which at only a thousand feet above sea level was a mere foothill compared with the heights further up the county. Where it scored over loftier places was in its prominence. It was visible from the coast only ten miles away and on a clear day the panoramic views from the top took in parts of eight Welsh and English counties. The approach roads to the village were few and poor, and this fact among others contributed to its distinctive character. Cardiff, the large, cosmopolitan university town and seaport to the south was another world, for there, a half-hour bus ride away, were the nearest cinemas and big shops. Yet although we marvelled at the sights and sounds of the city we came home to a place we loved deeply: a community that was culturally, socially, and to a great extent, linguistically, different. There were people who had lived in Cardiff for many years who wouldn't have recognised the Welsh language if they'd heard it. In our village, only six miles away up the hill, there lived a large number who hardly needed to speak English at all. At home, our father, a successfully self-educated man, switched with ease from one tongue to the other. Within our walls our mother used Welsh exclusively, except when there were monoglot English present.

'*Ble 'rwyt ti wedi bod 'nihyryn bach?*' said Mam, who could be censorious yet kind enough for you to be sure her anger was not permanent. 'Where have you been, you little scoundrel?' All the time knowing that I knew that she knew that I knew that she knew.

'*Gyda Walter yn y capel*,' I said, hoping that telling her I'd been at the chapel would satisfy her; even though it was Methodist rather than Congregationalist . . .

My father never worshipped at church or chapel; he performed his devotions at the bars of public houses. Mam only rarely showed impatience with his apparent mission of self-destruction; and then, not because of its effect upon *her*, but because of the wilful wastage of a brilliant brain.

Gareth in the meantime had washed his hands, face, and neck in the wooden tub which stood in the lean-to we called our back-kitchen, and was rubbing himself dry. He neatly folded the towel and placed it over the rack in front of what remained of the evening's fire, kissed Mam on the cheek and raised the latch of the staircase door, pausing only to wink at me and give the Scout salute.

My mother emerged from her reverie and with a glance at me said: 'Your brother looked all over for you.' Then, quietly: 'Were you there when your father stepped out of the pub tonight?'

'Yes,' I said, 'he was wonderful. The vicar nearly had a fit!' I looked up at her, hoping I'd said the right thing.

She turned away, her moist eyes catching the reflection of the lamp that hung from one of the old beams.

'Go to bed now,' she whispered. 'For he might be home shortly and he'll be sure to brag about it all night.' She hugged me and I followed Gareth up the winding stone staircase to our back bedroom.

Despite my fairly religious upbringing I was as sensitive as any of my peers to stories of the ghosts and the goblins that were always more powerful at night. I wouldn't have confessed such fears to Gareth, for he would have treated them with contempt.

Through the little half-open sashcord window above my bed I looked out at a beautiful pincushion sky. I covered my left eye and with the other could see the crescent of the May moon perfectly framed in the top left window pane. By changing hand and eye I could make the moon leap to the pane on the right. Such manoeuvres made me feel momentarily powerful. I decided no ghost or goblin was going to frighten *me* that night.

Across the room my brother had his head under the bed-clothes struggling to read in the fading light of a torch.

'Black up the window,' he said, putting a stop to my optical experiments.

I leant out of the window for a moment to savour the perfumes of elderflower and early honeysuckle. From high on the slopes of Garth Hill the repeated calls of a vixen were joined by the quavering hoots of a pair of tawny owls in the birchwood of Coed y Bedw. Before I had drawn the blackout curtains the local searchlights had begun their nightly lattice-work.

'*Brysia*,' 'Hurry up,' said Gareth. 'I want to light the candle.'

With one pull of the sash the window thumped shut and I dutifully placed the blackout sheet on its hooks. Soon the total darkness was relieved by a delicate glow. My brother, cupping the flame with his hand, placed the candlestick on the old bedside chest.

Lying on my side in feathery heaven I gazed across at Gareth, three years older and ten years wiser than me, as he read aloud from *The Count of Monte Cristo*. With each flick of a page the shadows danced about the small room, transforming familiar items into beings of fearsome intensity: the cracked, white-limed walls became wastelands transmuting a solitary moth into some unearthly creature of dark intent. I imagined I could see on the shelf above Gareth's bed Adolf Hitler, Josef Goebbels, and Hermann Goering staring down at me. Actually they were three jars of rhubarb wine.

From downstairs the voices of my father and the friends he had brought home from the pub droned on as a counter-point to my brother's continuing account of the adventures of Edmond Dantés.

Frequently the voices, obviously in deep debate, threw up baffling words like Darwinism; capitalism; pacifism; communism; fascism; Dunkirk; embarkation; warmongering. Clearly, my father had brought home friends who were likely to be Bertie Blake and Tommy Smitherham, for the talking was entirely in English.

There was much happening in the world beyond the window and I would soon have to start learning about it.

The shadows continued to dance and Gareth's voice was becoming more distant as I fell asleep.

Chapter Two

I pulled down the periscope and pressed my eye to the view-finder. The German battleship was square-on at about six hundred yards, a perfect target.

'Stand by to release torpedoes!' I commanded, flushed by a surge of adrenalin that threatened to wake me. I could see the senior officers standing stiffly on the upper deck, all giving the Nazi salute below a restless swastika flag; sitting German ducks if ever there'd been.

'Geraint!' A short pause, then *'Geraint!'* The dream would have to wait.

A small stone cracked against the bedroom window.

'GERAINT!'

As I unhooked the blackout sheet I noticed that Gareth had risen and gone. I sashed open the little window and pushed my head out into an already balmy summer morning. Walter was standing on the slabs of the bailey yard and preparing to throw another missile to rouse his lazy friend.

'Arf past bloody seven!' shouted Walter, dropping the stone and looking up appealingly. 'An' yew've forgotten it's Saturday, 'aven' yew!'

That did it! I was awake. Saturdays were special days. No school, for one thing. I didn't share my brother's enthusiasm for seats of learning, especially the village gaol some referred to as the local council school. I leapt into my top clothes and rushed downstairs, the stone steps cold against my bare feet.

I flew past Mam as she was laying the fire in the big room with the kindling-sticks I had gathered for her. Out in the back kitchen I unlocked the door to let Walter in and reached for my shoes.

'What's all this hurrying?' called my mother, still on her knees, bellowing the fire into life.

'Walter and I are going to see if we can find a few friends,' I said quickly, knowing instinctively the reason for my butty's early morning call.

'Not before you've done a few jobs for me,' she said, giving us a playful puff from the bellows.

Walter gave me an impatient look, but said, 'I'll 'elp Geraint, Mrs Llewellyn. To get the work done quicker, see.' Walter couldn't speak our native language, but had a knack of being able to understand simple exchanges.

'Bless you,' said my mother in English for Walter's benefit. 'Just draw some water for me and then you can go. But no mischief, mind!'

We each took a water-jack and made our way to the tap-house at the top of our street of eight dwellings, whose families were coming to life as we passed. Some of the menfolk had been up and away for hours, especially the coal miners who travelled to pits up the valley and the farm workers who crept out at dawn. My own father worked at the limestone quarry and would have been in his hut at six o'clock. Despite a previous night's alcohol he was never late for work.

We quickened our pace past Twm the Poacher's house, for he had dogs that could be very unfriendly. Even faster did we slip past Bopa Siân's door because of her unfortunate habit of collaring young people to run errands for her at awkward times.

We filled the jacks and started back, stopping every now and then to rest our aching arms, fearful that our plan to get away would be thwarted.

Back in the house, realizing I hadn't washed, I used some of the water for a swill and to clean my teeth in record time.

'What about your breakfast?' said my mother, noticing my anxiety. 'I won't let you go without your porridge.'

With a little push she gently but firmly guided us to the table in the back kitchen where the steaming gruel awaited. We sat down grudgingly, fully aware that there was no way to cool porridge quickly. Plenty of cold milk was applied, seemingly to little effect. We blew and blew and even took our dishes to the doorway, hoping that a draught would do the trick. The end of the month wouldn't come too soon, for then we would say goodbye to morning porridge. When it eventually cooled, we gulped it down and raced out into the world as my mother called out: 'No mischief, now!'

However, just around the corner, Temptation was lying in wait. Uncle Dai Lee the greengrocer had arrived; he had gone to one of the houses, leaving his cart blocking the lane. Old Bonni's head was buried in a nosebag from which we could hear the sounds of ancient teeth munching away. We squeezed through the narrow gap between the cart's side and the wall. Only a few months ago the vehicle had been regularly filled with a rich variety of fruit, whose mouth-watering aromas were ever evocative of exotic faraway lands. I would gaze longingly at an inviting aggregation of peaches, plums, pomegranates, bunches of purple grapes, and fat bananas. Now the only hint of the exotic came from a couple of items that had escaped the U-Boats: a dusty sack of monkey nuts and a box of Jaffa oranges concealed by a cloth from prying eyes and idle hands. I raised the cloth and gazed at the oranges. Each one was wrapped in soft white tissue paper and I had just started to fondle one when Walter snapped: *'No mischief, mind!'*

We hurried off again, soon to arrive at the Twyn mound where we took a breather and gathered our thoughts. After a minute or two Walter produced a handful of monkey nuts and offered me some.

'*Lleidar*!' I said, feigning horror.

'That means thief, dunnit?'

'Aye, and *you'll* probably end up in Cardiff Gaol like your uncle Dic last Christmas!'

'It was only 'olly he pinched,' said Walter, looking hurt.

'True,' I said, 'but he whipped it from the *church*.'

''E don't go to church,' said Walter.

'No', I said, fancying a bit of cruelty, 'only to remove things. It'll be the collection box next.'

Walter looked glum and turned his head away. I thought it was a good moment to come clean, so I tapped his shoulder and took from under my shirt the best Jaffa orange this side of Palestine.

'*Yew sod*!' whooped my friend in crime. We were still giggling as we romped off towards Nant yr Arian farm.

The sun had climbed and I wished that I was wearing lighter clothes. But at least I had shoes. Walter still wore boots of the kind we all had to use in winter: heavy, hobnailed, and hot. But we were lucky. At our age our grandfathers ran barefoot during their precious leisure time, saving their clogs for the hours of toil both above and below ground. Yet, as we looked about, we saw and heard things much as our forefathers did: the steady swishing of the scythe, and the flapping of birds fleeing as hay or corn fell in wavy patterns; the squeaks and scrapes of iron-rimmed wheels of carts on stony roads; a braying donkey or a whinnying mare, and all around us the melancholy bleating of sheep. The sounds of centuries. When this harmony was rudely interrupted by the sound of a car or a lorry we still didn't fully appreciate that it was a taste of future horrors. Now, though, there were new noises that at once excited and puzzled us.

Awesome sounds. Reaching the mountain road we detected rumblings from the sky.

'What's Welsh for thunder?' Walter asked.

'*Tyrfa*, we say around here,' I replied. 'Some say *taran*.'

'Fancy 'avin' two words for the same thing!'

'Oh, there's more,' I said, but I was interrupted by Walter gripping my arm and pointing skywards. Fifty or more dots appeared in the distance, like migrating geese, but making a different sound. Soon the dots became blobs that turned into what we were afraid of – bombers!

'Christ!' shouted Walter. 'Bloody Germans! They've come to get us. They're going to bomb the bloody village!'

Like Walter, I was looking for somewhere to dive for safety before the swarm passed over. We could see clearly the RAF roundels on the sides of the few aeroplanes that weren't completely camouflaged.

'I wonder where they're going?' we said simultaneously, trying to disguise immense relief. It wasn't referred to again until Walter suggested that the RAF were asking for trouble by putting 'bullseyes' on the sides of their 'planes.

The track known as 'Lovers' Avenue' threaded its way through bracken on the lower breast of Garth Hill. Where it intersected the high thorn hedge known as Clawdd Arthur, there stood, appropriately, a sturdy kissing gate.

We reached the dry-stone wall above Nant yr Arian and sat in a clump of bracken to discuss our next move. By removing one of the capstones from the wall we had a clear view of the whole yard, whence the clinking of pails and the occasional grunt from Ianto Protheroe told us that the morning's milking was over.

A sheepdog sat scratching itself by the farmhouse door, but all else was still.

'D' yew think she's in there?' whispered Walter.

'Mrs Protheroe, you mean?' I answered, trying to sound casual.

'Don't be bloody stupid, Geraint, yew *know* who I do mean! I've come 'ere for the same damn' reason as yew 'ave – an' yew know it!'

The cloudless sky was becoming bluer by the minute. We lay on our backs and felt warmth from the earth. Seductive scents of summer teased our nostrils: pleasantly pungent emissions from the ferns only just maintaining supremacy over various odours wafting from the farmyard below. Two cuckoos duetted in the valley, while high above our heads a circling buzzard mewed. Nearby a solitary bee hovered, surveyed us, decided against a suicidal sting, and buzzed away to a clump of buttercups. Life glows at such times. I began to daydream, dozily thinking about what heroisms I could perform to impress girls with tortoises. I would get the pony from my uncle's farm and ride to Nant yr Arian dressed as a knight. I would come galloping and with one swift move take the girl around the waist and hoist her up behind me. I was wondering what exactly I would do with the pet she'd be likely to have with her when we were roused by a clattering of metal buckets on the cobbled yard.

'*Myn uffarn i! Iesu Mawr! Uffarn gola!*' blasphemed Ianto as he bent to pick up an overturned bucket. 'By hell! Jesus!'

The farmer had accidentally kicked over a full pail of milk that was now running all over the cobbles.

'Well,' said Walter. 'That's buggered it, we daren't go down there now!'

Somehow I felt relieved for I hadn't relished the idea of going to knock on the farmhouse door. What would I have said? Possibly: 'Excuse me, Mrs Protheroe, may we see the pretty girl you have staying with you?' Or: 'We've brought some lettuce for the tortoise!'

I felt my cheeks go hot as the farmhouse door opened. However, no vision of loveliness emerged – only Mrs Protheroe, who looked at the mess and shook her head.

'I'll tell yew what,' said Walter, with a wry smile, 'I dare yew to go down and tell 'er it's no use bloody cryin' over spilt milk!'

We were about to abandon our mission when one last look towards the farm revealed the object of our quest standing in the middle of the yard. Mrs Protheroe had joined her husband in the shed, the noises emerging thence suggesting she might have had her hands around his throat. The girl we'd come to see was standing out in the yard, tortoiseless. So taken was I with her serenity and poise that I vowed there and then to devote my life to her.

'Christ, she looks just like Shirley Temple,' said Walter.

'No. She's *much* better than that,' I said.

The beautiful girl turned and slowly walked back to the door. I took the Jaffa orange from its wrapper and flung it in her direction, hoping it would land at her feet. It bounced off the wall and rolled over the cobblestones. Its arrival at the edge of the manure heap coincided with the emergence of the herd from the cowshed and the fruit quickly became a glutinous mess of dung, milk, and juice. Any romantic thoughts I might have retained were temporarily shelved.

'Don't know why we bothered,' mumbled Walter to himself as we picked our way back to the village. 'Only cissies want to be friends with girls,' he added.

That stung, and I was about to dig him in the ribs when he continued: 'I don't suppose she'd want to talk to a cripple, anyway.'

I reminded him that she'd spoken to us in the vestry and brought us food. We brightened and quickened our pace, Walter dragging his leg like a speedway rider.

By the time we reached the Twyn mound there were groups of village kids and evacuees playing together happily. There was much tumbling, pushing, and poking going on among the younger ones, while other groups stood chatting.

'Cor, yer darn awf tawk fanny darn eeah!'

'Warrabout yew 'en? Why do yew speak like *yew* do do!'

'I'll swop yer wan jennywoine piece of Gerry shrapnel for that pen-knife you got theyah'.

'Yew gorrope. It's my dad's.'

'Wha' goimes d'you play darn eeah then?'

'Rugby mostly. Fox an' 'ounds on winter nights. Cricket an' Bomparino all year round.'

'Woss that Bompyreenow then?'

'Strong 'orses an' weak donkeys.'

Fuller explanations would come later, but for the time being a ritual of introduction would have to be seen through to its end if the promising friendships being formed were to have any permanence. Soon bags of glass marbles appeared and teams were picked. Playballs flew skyward and a frenzy of whipping tops spun patterns of colour on the smooth rock slabs. Walter and I searched in vain for the boy we'd seen with the boxing gloves the night before. We asked around but no one seemed to know the family to which he'd beeen allocated. We did a few handstands and, as nobody seemed to have noticed, we wandered away.

'Mam will be expecting me home for dinner soon,' I said, as we reached the lane behind the blacksmith's. 'It's twelve o' clock already.'

'See yew this afternoon then, Ger,' called Walter as we parted in the lane. 'Meet yew outside Pegler's shop.'

The mid-day sun was hot, so I chose to walk in the cool shadow of the thorn hedge down the side of the lane that bounded the smithy yard. From the forge I could hear the thump-thump of Wil Refail's hammer changing to tap-tap and then tinkle-tinkle as a horseshoe cooled and took shape. A hiss as shoe met hoof tempted me to go in just for a smell and a chat. The blacksmith spoke superb Welsh and was an able versifier. I was too young for the poetry but I loved being regaled with stories of the childhood tricks he used to play with my maternal grandfather. However, Mam didn't like me being late for anything, so this time I just made my way home.

My pace quickened past the wall of Horeb Chapel graveyard, for burial grounds were not my favourite places, even in daylight. I could see the tops of tombstones above the wall: dark, lichen-covered slabs that I knew had Welsh inscriptions commending spirits to the safekeeping of the Almighty. Looking up I was dazzled by the sun and instantly one of the tombstones seemed to uproot itself, to clear the wall and land in the lane right in front of me. It was no tombstone. It was Dilwyn Price-Davies.

'Where's Quasimodo?' he demanded.

Trembling, I managed to answer. 'His name is Walter. He's not a hunchback. He's a sort of cripple and he's my best friend.'

Dilwyn's right fist split my lip and I tasted blood.

As I ducked to avoid his left, something flew through the air, took hold of Dilwyn and pulled him to the ground. Walter was as wild as a mad cat.

I joined in and tried to grab Dilwyn's hair.

'Go home!' said Walter between blows; which, I confess, seemed quite a good idea. I couldn't leave him, but even the two of us were really no match for the merciless bully. Only the sound of approaching voices saved us from further distress, and before the group of village kids and evacuees came into sight Dilwyn had vanished.

After the gang had passed we began to lick our wounds. I was much bloodied and Walter's left cheek was badly bruised.

'Thank you, Walter,' I said. 'I don't know what would have happened if you hadn't turned up.'

'Thassalright,' said my brave friend. 'Yew were lucky I'd dropped my penknife by 'ere somewhere when I was talkin' to yew. I came back for it. Fat chance of findin' it, though.'

On the way home I stopped at the tap-house to bathe my nose and mouth. I held my head in the stream of cold water. It stung like nettles.

Gareth was the first to see me when I timidly entered the house. After a moment of shocked silence he came over, wrapped his arms around me, shouted for our mother, and said, *'Beth digwyddodd, 'mrawd annwyl?'* 'For God's sake what's happened, brother?'

'Fell off a wall,' I said, through split lips.

My bloodstained shirt would have been bad enough, but when she saw my face, my mother looked as if she might collapse.

'I knew it, I knew it, I just *knew* something was going to happen.' She held me close.

'It's down to Doctor Glennie with you straight away. *Mae eisiau pwythau ar hwn.* You need stitching!'

Gareth was sent ahead to tell the doctor we were coming. It was a three-mile walk that would take us about an hour, but Gareth would run it five times quicker.

There was no time for a change of clothes or a proper wash. We headed off towards Creigiau, the tiny hamlet in our parish where Elizabeth Glennie the Scots doctor lived. The shortest route was along the footpath that wound its way down through a majestic beechwood that accommodated a large and noisy community of rooks. Today they were as vocal as ever, seeming to be mocking us as we passed, and I was glad when we had picked up the path that skirted the meadows where the rabbits were. The gate clanged shut behind us sending dozens of them running for cover.

'*Rhaid i mi ofyn i Twm am weningan rhyw ddiwrnod hefyd,*' muttered my mother as we proceeded. 'That reminds me, I must ask Twm the Poacher to bring us a rabbit.'

Dogs barked loudly as we passed Penllwyn Cynfyn farm. In my light-headed state I wondered if they could smell me. By the time we reached the little copse at Graig yr Ŷd I was a bit delirious. Behind every tree was a savage predator ready to pounce; on every branch a serpent uncoiled and threatened. Wild-eyed weasels and wildcats, stoats and polecats, were watching and waiting . . .

Gareth was waiting for us outside the doctor's house.

'Your brother's been fainting off,' said Mam. 'I've had to half-carry him this last mile.'

We scrunched our way up a seemingly endless gravel path. By the time we reached the doctor's front door my delirium had subsided somewhat, but the pair of crows on a nearby tree reminded me of vultures.

'So, laddie! Fall off a wee wall did we? *Really!*' Soothing though the doctor's voice was, I felt uneasy as I noticed the instruments that lay on a small table nearby. My mother and my brother gripped my hands comfortingly as the needle went in, the pain from each of the seven stitches making me want to cry out.

'Well, isn't that the prettiest embroidery you'll ever see,' said Doctor Glennie. 'And to think I cannae sew clothes for toffee.' I had no idea what she meant but I felt safe in her hands. She smiled. 'I think ye'll be drinking through a straw tonight.'

As she was preparing some medicine for me the doctor was whispering something to my mother. Athough I missed much of it I could clearly hear '. . . and watch out for signs of shock.'

The pain had subsided a little and I was beginning to enjoy the special attention. I looked forward to showing off my battle-wounds to my friends.

'Right, Mrs Louellen,' said the doctor, and I am sure my mother, for once, didn't resent the mispronunciation. 'You can release the prisoner. Come along now, and I'll drive you home.'

A ride in a motor car! This would make all the pain worth-while.

Gareth sat in the back with my mother and I was allowed up front. It was only the second time I had been in a car, the first being the occasion of my grandfather's funeral. The leather-lined luxury of the doctor's Austin 10 was of another world. Car owners often had lawn mowers too. Some of them actually had lawns. Such families had running water on tap *inside* their houses, as well as carpets and vacuum cleaners and people who came in to do the washing. Yet as far as I knew there was no envy; those who had, had – and the rest of us did without.

I sank into the polished leather seat and the doctor invited me to press the starter button, which task I was pleased to perform.

We were home in less than ten minutes. Before she left the doctor was thanked profusely – and I was put to bed.

'Go and fetch your father from the Twyn before he gets too drunk,' said my mother, and Gareth sprinted off.

Usually on a Saturday my father wouldn't have come home until midnight, his vocal cords thoroughly lubricated. It would be two o'clock or even three on the Sunday morning before we could sleep. His performances were usually for the benefit of friends he brought home, but sometimes just for his patient wife. If alone, he would still carry on. I'd heard lengthy passages from *Hamlet* several times and I felt I knew 'The Wreck Of The Hesperus' backwards. He knew all the popular songs of the day and would alternate these with sections from the Welsh opera *Hywel a Blodwen*, when he would sing both the tenor and soprano parts. It was better than listening to the wireless. He was never aggressive, but occasionally his performance would degenerate into pathetic rambling. At such times my mother would seek our assistance in putting him to bed. I hated the smell of the drink on him and longed for him to mend his ways and become like other fathers: sober, modest, and boring. My friends all wanted their fathers to be like mine.

I raised my head upon hearing the release of the stairs-door latch. My father and Gareth came into the room. Dad, shocked to see the state of my face, came over and sat at the bottom of the bed. It was a while before he spoke, but he was obviously fairly sober.

'Can you talk?' he asked eventually. I nodded.

'Scouts' honour?' he said. 'Did you really fall off a wall?'

'I'm not in the Scouts.'

'Cubs' honour, then!'

I pretended that I couldn't speak further, and he decided not to press the matter, apart from muttering that he would expect the truth from me in due course.

'Come downstairs,' he said. 'You'll be better off down there.'

I needed no further persuasion and in two ticks I was on my way down.

My father was on form that night: not too garrulous, not too demonstrative, just brilliantly entertaining; and all for my benefit.

He wound up the gramophone and put on a Fred Astaire record. Then he proceeded to tap-dance around the table, onto chairs, making magic with his bowler hat and ivory-handled walking stick. He did impressions of stars of the wireless Arthur Askey and Richard Murdoch, but his speciality was Winston Churchill. Fearful that my laughter would burst my stitches, my father slowed down to begin some story-telling. I had heard some of the tales before but was about to become acquainted with a few others.

I drank soup through a straw while my father told stories that had been handed down through the ages. There were abominable creatures such as the *Ladi Wen*, who sat on the branches of trees and terrified people. Then the *Ceffyl Dŵr*, the white horse that would tempt the timid to climb onto its back, whereupon it would fly away with its rider only to eventually dash him to the rocks below. I was always scared by tales of *Y Toeli*, The Ghost Funeral, a phantom procession that passed by at night, supposedly presaging a fatality in the family of the person who beheld it.

My mother's protestations that such tales were not fit to be told in a Christian household didn't deter my father. He emphasised that whilst the stories were not based on fact it was important that I should learn all aspects of our folklore. Through all this my brother had been deeply buried in *The Count of Monte Cristo*; reaching the last page he closed the book at about half-past-nine.

A couple of readings from the fine poems of Eifion Wyn out of my father's leather-bound copy of *Telynegion Maes a Môr* brought the evening's entertainment to a close. Now there would be a hot bath and supper to put an end to a truly eventful day.

A determined rat-tat-tat on the back door jackknifed me upright in the tin tub. I was relieved to discern from the ensuing chatter that it was only Edwards the special constable checking on blackouts. I relaxed and continued to scrub myself with the pumice stone. The arrival of visitors at inopportune times was a natural hazard faced by those of us who had no choice but to bath in our living rooms. There was always a steady stream of callers at our house, none of whom I would have wished to see me as God had made me.

My father discussed the progress of the war with the bobby before waving him goodbye and coming back into the room. 'That uniform has gone to his head,' he muttered, touching his temple with a forefinger, thereby indicating that the man might be in of need psychiatric help. 'I'm sure he believes we are sending messages to the Germans from our back-kitchen.' Edwards had noticed a tiny chink of light escaping from our pantry window and had felt it his duty to warn us of the dire consequences which could result from such neglect. I removed the last soapsuds from my back and pondered how many elite Luftwaffe squadrons were leaving some German airfield at that very moment, having received news of our carelessness. Could the might of the German air force now be concentrated on an all-out attack on our back-kitchen? I suddenly realised that I was starving.

In the manner of nursing an infant, Mam was holding a loaf to her aproned bosom, slicing the bread with long strokes reminiscent of a fiddler. Gareth, already fully scrubbed and combed, was sitting at the table, tucking into large slices of brown bread mortared together with thick layers of margarine and strawberry jam. My father now sat at the fire, toasting small pieces of cheese on the end of a long, crudely constructed wire fork. One of the heavenly smells is of cheese slowly toasting above a coal fire. As the drips hissed and spat amid the flames, my father would expertly twist the fork, and, gauging the precise degree of browning, would withdraw the slice of cheese to place it upon the bread that was waiting to receive it on my plate. Towel tucked around me, I sat down and prepared to feast. I applied an appropriate amount of brown sauce and took a bite. I cried out in pain but hunger forced me to continue.

'Warm milk it'll be for you next time,' said my mother, as she put her arm around me. 'I should have known.'

Dad listened to the nine o'clock news on his beloved Phillips wireless set that sat on the corner shelf. It seemed to have an almost human face: two mesh-covered apertures for eyes and a large bulbous tuning knob for a nose, below which stations from Hilversum to Luxembourg were rows of teeth in a smiling mouth. It was easy to believe that the set itself was speaking.

With a shake of the head and some muttered comment about the threat of invasion, my Saturday-night-sober father turned off the wireless and reached for the book he was currently reading. He slumped into his chair and was soon aboard *The Beagle* with Charles Darwin en route to the Galapagos Islands. I found myself yawning, which brought more pain from my stitches. Then Gareth and I went to bed, but not before each of us had given our mother a good hug.

Climbing the stone stairs I began for the first time to consider what to do about Dilwyn. The next day was Sunday and I wondered if I should really be thinking of forgiving him. But tomorrow would be soon enough to think about that. Now I was too tired. I got into bed and was soon asleep.

Chapter Three

My occasional nightmares were always more than simply un-pleasant; however, the latest was by far the most frightful. An implacable army of hungry and highly malignant tortoises was coming at me from all directions. I had no means of escape and it was only when they were closing in over the last twenty yards or so and me with my back against the wall of Pegler's shop that I found screaming with a stitched-up lip to be extremely painful.

I woke with my heart beating a tattoo and Gareth applying a cold wet flannel to my forehead.

'How are you feeling, soldier?' said my brother.

'I'm all right *now*,' I said, with a deep sigh of relief. 'But what a hellish dream!'

'Fine,' said Gareth with a smile. 'Now you can get up for breakfast.'

Seeing from the clock on the shelf that it was only half-past-six, I told him to clear off back to bed and leave me in peace. Before doing so he removed the blackout, leaving me to feel that the early morning sunshine had never been so welcome.

The men's voices in the lane below were loud and urgent. I knew instinctively what had happened: Mr Cadwalader was out again. The veteran of World War One suffered from chronic 'brainstorms', that, oddly enough, were almost always nocturnal. He would remove all his nightclothes and, leaving his sleeping wife, would slip silently out and away into the darkness, naked as a jaybird. Mornings would find him sitting on a garden wall or halfway up a tree, often waving his arms and ranting loudly, his rambling harangues – usually to First World War personnel – punctuated by much coughing and spitting. One memorable occasion saw him captured astride one of the Garth Mountain's ack-ack guns, cursing and reviling the 'lazy, shiny-arsed bastards' who were responsible for the shortage of desperately-needed ammunition. Now, however, it seemed that his anger was directed mostly against General Haig, and his bilingual cursing and swearing included many words and expressions that were new to me.

His long-suffering wife Ceridwen rejected the oft-repeated suggestion that Mr C could be tied to his bed after retiring, on the grounds that it would be 'undignified'. Well, being brought home by half-a-dozen men after a 'night out', albeit with an *ad hoc* blanket covering one's nakedness, could hardly be said to be dignified. Now, as we had done on previous occasions, Gareth and I watched the return of the wanderer from our bedroom window.

'Cad druan,' said Gareth, half to himself. 'Poor Cad. He should be in some kind of . . . home.'

Four men were carrying the old soldier with two others walking alongside. Cad was a very strong man who had been known to break free from his captors and rush off.

From the shelf on the landing I took down my father's Lee-Enfield, the First World War relic with which he had been issued before the LDV became the Home Guard. The five-round clasp of bullets had been safely hidden, but I was allowed to handle the rifle. Resting it on the window ledge I pointed it at the men in the lane. Then I shot each man in turn. *Click:* Mr Lewis, the roadsweeper. *Click:* Mr Roberts, the waterman. *Click:* Mr Rhys, the rent-collector. *Click:* Dammit! I think I missed Mr Smitherham . . .

'Put that gun away, brat!' said Gareth. 'You've been seeing too many cowboy pictures.'

Scrubbed clean and in our best clothes we were ready for Sunday morning service. Our father didn't disapprove of our attending chapel; in fact he always said it was a good thing to hear both sides of a story.

As soon as we had left my father would get down to his own Sunday devotions. For some time he had been following a Bennett College correspondence course and was cramming a week's work into every Sabbath. For some reason he never drank beer on a Sunday; not because the pubs were closed – for he could easily have joined one of the local working men's clubs. He had diplomas in several subjects including English, even though it wasn't his first language. Now he was following a Science course specialising in 'Limes and Cements', a subject in which he had good reason to be interested. We knew that he was desperate to rise above his lowly-paid job as quarry foreman, for, at thirty-nine, he could see many of his contemporaries enjoying a more affluent lifestyle. He wasn't envious – simply regretful of wasted opportunities.

There had been an unpromising start to his working life. At thirteen he had started work down a pit at Trehafod on the day his best friend was killed underground. At sixteen he was in the First World War – an experience he never spoke of. Later he worked on roads and on building sites. He also occasionally helped out at his cousin's farm where his skill with horses was put to good use.

By the time he married he had settled at the quarry and was soon a foreman. He quickly realized that he was the intellectual equal of his student engineer colleagues who, in turn, were to wonder why a man so knowledgeable about limestone should be only one step up from a labourer.

At Bronllwyn the morning service was always held in the vestry that easily accommodated the thirty-or-so regulars. Gareth and I held the door open for Mam. Inside, Illtyd Probert, who was already standing out front, spotted us, pointed to me, and called out: 'Ah, Geraint! The Bibles! You know where they are.'

I always dreaded this for it meant going on my own into the main chapel, but it was my turn and I couldn't be seen to hesitate. I felt a chill as I went through the door that connected the vestry to the rather ghostly main chamber that was dank and smelt of furniture polish. I recalled the majestic sounds I'd occasionally heard there: glorious harmonies and stirring hymns telling of the treasures in store for us in heaven. I had also heard preachers roaring about sin, suffering, and damnation.

I opened the little cupboard door beneath the pulpit, took out an armful of the black books, and returned to the vestry. No one said anything about my stitched-up lips, not even in chapel whispers.

At the front row I froze. There, tucked in between Mr and Mrs Protheroe, sat the girl of my dreams! She smiled sweetly as I nervously passed her a Bible.

All heads were bent as Mr Probert began a solemn prayer. As he asked our heavenly Father for mercy and thanked Him for His bountiful gifts, I strained to get a better view of the girl whose golden hair glistened in the light from the vestry window. Old Illtyd droned on and I wondered how the girl must be feeling, as she couldn't have understood a word of what the preacher was saying.

'*O Arglwydd* . . .' 'Oh Lord, we thank thee for the Holy Scriptures that arm our souls to resist the temptations of this world . . . the flesh . . . the devil . . .'

The preacher's words were punctuated with '*Ie, ie!*' – 'Yes, yes!' from a few excited members of the congregation.

Finally, as always, Illtyd paused with inclined head and closed eyes for a good half-minute, during which the silence was broken by a cough or two from the pews and the alarm call of a blackbird through the vestry window.

Eventually the harmonium, even more ancient than the one at the Methodist house up the road, introduced the hymn. Normally I would have helped the time pass by watching Mrs Probert's spindly legs and tiny feet fighting with the pedals, but now my gaze was directed elsewhere and I was disappointed to lose sight of the girl as everyone rose to sing.

> *'I bob un sydd ffyddlon, dan ei faner Ef,*
> *Mae gan Iesu goron fry yn Nheyrnas Nef.'*

'For every faithful follower beneath His banner
Jesus awaits with a crown in Heaven's kingdom high.'

Oh, the bass voices of Wil Shanco and Twm Tonmawr rising like a dark tide! My mother's contralto, together with that of Shênad Watcyn and others, richly complemented the sopranos, whose crystal quality was only slightly impaired by the contribution of Mrs Protheroe, who was just a little too loud. The silvery tenor voices included that of Siôn Williams the grocer, who, as always, stood with his right hand hidden behind the left side of his jacket. Gareth had once described Siôn's Napoleonic stance to our father, who replied that the grocer was probably checking his wallet.

My brother was called up front to read a lesson, which he regularly performed with distinction. Understandably our mother was very proud of him.

I tried hard to tear my eyes away from the girl four rows in front, even though I could see only the back of her head. I thought: 'Wait till I tell Walter!'

After the service groups gathered outside the chapel to bid farewells, and to my great joy the Protheroes paused to speak to my mother.

'These are my evacuees,' said the farmer's wife much as she would have described day-old chicks. 'This is Ronnie Webb and his sister Annabel.'

It was the first time for me to really notice the boy who had been with them in the chapel. He was about my brother's age and it slowly dawned upon me that this was the lad who'd been carrying boxing gloves as he stepped off the bus on Friday.

'Say hello, then,' murmured my mother, giving me a nudge.

'Hello, Ronnie,' I said.

Another nudge. 'Hello, Annabel,' I said.

Gareth joined us and was introduced.

'You've got a funny name,' said Annabel with a smile, *'Gerunt*, or something.'

'It's Geraint,' I said. 'A Welsh name. Dates back to the Ancient Britons. I'm quite proud of it.'

'What happened to *him*?' said Mr Protheroe to my mother. 'His face looks as if it's been in a gin-trap.'

Looking at me, my mother replied, 'He fell off a wall. At least that's *his* story.'

'Been in a fight, more like,' said the farmer. 'Boys around here are devils for the fighting. It's about time we organised proper boxing for them.'

I was pleased that they weren't speaking in English, for I wouldn't have wanted Annabel to hear those comments. Anyway, the state of my face hadn't appeared to interest her.

Meanwhile, Gareth and Ronnie were getting on well and talking excitedly. They were about the same age and clearly shared an interest in boxing, for I could hear . . . 'Farr, Louis, Galento, Carnera . . . '

People began to make for home, and I felt sorry as the Protheroes' cart creaked off towards Nant yr Arian. Mam had gone on ahead, for she would have to cook a dinner for four within the hour. I went with Gareth and we took a short cut across the rugby field that backed onto the lane behind our terrace. Although I *tried* to stop thinking of Annabel, the image of her lovely face persisted.

I walked on, confident that no-one had noticed my pre-occupation. Now and then I would kick at a daisy, leap over a cow-pat, and start whistling.

'You are in love, brother,' said Gareth.

With a deft hand-off my brother parried the kick to his backside before I chased him the length of the field.

The glad feeling when Gareth promised 'not to tell' continued throughout dinner. The pain in my lip had begun to ease and eating was becoming more enjoyable. In any case, food was rarely left on plates in our house. Cooking could never have been easy for my mother with only one oven for roasting and an open coal fire for boiling water and vegetables. But her meals were always delightful.

On Sunday afternoons in summer the village snoozed, coming to life again at dusk. The evening was walking time. As they passed in the lanes families exchanged pleasantries, stopping occasionally to discuss the latest news about babies, sickness, death, and letters from relatives in the services. Not infrequently, from behind hands in front of mouths, unimaginable gossip was whispered into eager ears.

What was being said? A plague of locusts in the Vale of Glamorgan? The Black Death in Barry? The Germans landing at Lavernock? Whatever it was, it wasn't for juvenile ears, and no amount of cajoling could persuade parents to tell. But I had my own item of interest now and I itched to tell Walter. At the end of the afternoon I called at his house. This was in a terrace at the lower end of Pengarth, where all the families seemed to be large. I knocked on the door and was called inside, having to step past a variety of cats before reaching the living room, where Walter, his mother, father, and two elder sisters seemed to be festooned with babies, kittens, and pups.

'Yewer friend 'ave come for yew!' shouted Mr Hopkins above the noise to his eldest son. Walter nodded, but couldn't speak because a woollen bootie was being stuffed into his mouth by a baby brother. Elsewhere other dramas were being enacted by a tumble of children, one of whom was sitting on the floor with a loaf of bread and dangerously wielding a large saw-knife. The scene reminded me of a Breughel I'd seen in the Art Gallery of the National Museum of Wales.

Walter's mother was hanging clothes onto a rail in front of a large open fire. Their vapours combined with other none-too-savoury odours to produce a very 'homely' atmosphere, described eloquently by Walter as we came out: 'Terrible in there, mun! Smells like a baby's pram – all piss an' broken biscuits!'

'I wish I lived in a clean 'ouse like yewers,' said Walter as we made our way up Heol y Pentre.

I made no reply; instead, I said, 'I've seen her! *And* spoken to her!'

'Who, for Christ's sake?'

'The girl. Annabel!'

Walter was quiet, so I said, 'You know, *our* girl.'

'So *what*?'

'So every-bloody-thing! That's what!' I said, disappointed by his apparent indifference.

Walter smiled, 'Look, Ger, she's *yewer* girl really. Not mine. I'm really not interested, see.'

'Thank you,' I said, 'that's OK then.' Of course it didn't occur to me that Annabel might have had other ideas . . .

We ambled across to the Twyn mound where we sat on one of the limestone slabs and spent an hour devising ways for wreaking vengeance on Dilwyn. Eventually we agreed that one of *my* ideas, if only for its sheer gruesomeness, was by far the most appealing. We would strip a pair of tall, springy saplings, bend them over, and tie them together with a short length of rope fixed to a stout peg hammered into the ground. The captive would be placed between the two trees with his left leg tied to one and his right to the other. The rope would then be cut and two Dilwyns sent to eternity. It seemed that the previous night's spirit of forgiveness had well and truly departed.

'*That's* a bloody good 'un!' said Walter. ''Ow did yew dream that one up?'

'I saw it in a Tarzan picture,' I confessed. 'And now it makes me feel sick.'

'Me, too,' said Walter. 'And anyway, we're supposed to *forgive* our enemies, aren't we?'

'That's right.'

'So do we forgive Dilwyn, then?'

'Well, it *is* Sunday.'

'Yes, but *really* forgive 'im, I mean. Like for ever.'

'What do *you* think?'

'I asked *yew* first. Yew are the one who goes to chapel.'

'That's got nothing to do with it,' I lied.

By the time we parted company it was almost dark. This time I didn't go home through the Refail lane: I ran like a deer across Penygarn field, climbed the wall at the bottom of our garden, and entered the house by the back door to receive a gentle admonishment from my mother.

'I was just about to send Gareth to find you,' she said.

My brother looked up from his homework and gave me a wink. Dammit, I thought, I'm sure he thinks I've been out with a girlfriend!

My father was stretched out on his chair, snoring gently. By his side on a small table lay a number of textbooks.

My mother put a finger to her mouth. 'Let him sleep,' she whispered. But a few moments later my father was fully awake, roused by the warning drone of the air-raid siren.

My mother quickly grabbed some cushions and blankets and directed Gareth and me towards the pantry. After fetching his rifle from upstairs my father put on his Home Guard overcoat and was away down the garden path.

Our pantry measured about six feet square. It had white-washed walls and a large stone slab beneath which my brother and I took refuge during air-raids.

Somewhat to the annoyance of our mother Gareth had insisted on finishing his essay before making for the pantry, but after we were both ensconced in our little cave Mam closed the door and returned to the living room, probably to pray.

Gareth and I spoke in whispers, the better to be able to listen to any interesting sounds that might be coming from the sky.

After a few minutes we heard gunfire. First, several sharp bangs from the Garth batteries, followed by *boomphs* as the bigger coastal guns opened up. Then we heard the hum of aircraft and recognised the engine-throb of Heinkel 111s. Occasionally we would hear the whistle of a descending bomb and a massive explosion. Gareth reckoned the attacks were on Cardiff Docks and Treforest Trading Estate.

The noise gradually subsided, but it was a full half-hour before the 'all-clear' was heard. My mother, wrapped in her shawl and looking pale, asked us to go into the front bedroom and take a peep through the window. The fiery glow in the sky over Cardiff was clearly visible above the high ground of Cae-rhiw.

Dad came back at about one a.m. to say that Cardiff had taken a pounding and that there were probably many casualties. Gareth and I had heard him coming in and we'd slipped down the stone steps to eavesdrop behind the stairs door. We'd all been a bit worried about him.

Sleep was a fairly long time coming that night. Quite apart from thinking about the air-raid, I couldn't help wondering how all the evacuees would fit into our little school in the morning.

Chapter Four

Before going to school on a Monday morning Walter and I usually met to collect groceries from Pegler's shop. Even on the dreariest days Walter would brighten the place up. This was one of those mornings.

Mr Smitherham was smiling as he stood behind the counter with his hands in his overall pockets. Leaning forward to face Walter, he said, 'So, young man! What'll it be for you, then?'

Walter put on his best Buster Keaton face. 'Ten pounds of taters with eyes in 'em should see us through the week.'

'Cans't beat 'em old jokes, 'sno,' laughed Smitherham. 'But it takes a knack like you'm got to tell 'em well!'

At eight-thirty we met again and ran through rain to the school. The playground was as alive as a cattle market, for the number of pupils had more than doubled. At nine o'clock a shrill whistle brought everyone through the main entrance to pack the hall for the headmaster's welcoming address.

William David, to whom the education of Pengarth children was entrusted, was not a very popular person. Only now, with the benefit of hindsight, can I even begin to analyse, let alone solve, the enigma that was 'Eaglebeak'. Adults saw him as an obscure figure who declined involvement in village life outside the school; apart, that is, from the Observer Corps, of which he was an assiduous but apparently argumentative member. Few children liked him. For most he was an ogre, a tyrant without a single redeeming feature. But it would be churlish to begrudge the man some praise for the way in which he accommodated the host of evacuees that had so suddenly descended upon him.

We sat on the floor in rows, the youngest in front and the giants of Standard Seven at the back. The air was heavy with the smell of wet clothes. Three evacuee teachers were sitting out front with the usual school staff. Eaglebeak fumbled for the silver fob dangling from his waistcoat and took out his watch, giving it a typically grave examination before returning it to his pocket. He cleared his throat and rose to his feet.

'I have a solemn yet very happy duty to perform this day – to welcome to the school our new friends from afar. You, the children of Chatham, are a long way from home, but I trust that your stay with us will enrich your lives and provide you with many happy memories. No doubt, the sounds of last night's air-raid over Cardiff were all too familiar to you, and we hope that Hermann Goering and his cronies will not pester us too much, and that your time here will be peaceful. A word now to the natives of this parish. You must make our new friends very welcome. They are away from their homes and their parents and they will need you to help them settle in.'

It occurred to me that these were the kindest words I'd ever heard from our headmaster. I thought that he might have been putting on a show for the evacuee teachers.

Then suddenly I thought of Annabel. Where was she? Would she be in my class? Would Ronnie be there? Or was *he* at the Grammar School with my brother? I looked around, but could see neither him nor his sister.

'There we are, then,' said Eaglebeak. 'It remains only for me to introduce our new teachers: Mrs Brownham, Mr Trotter, and Mr Black.'

The three stood up, smiled at the room, and sat down.

'Oh, and just one more thing,' said the headmaster. He flexed his cane. 'Disobedience of *any* kind will not be tolerated from *any* pupil. I understand that the school from which you evacuees have come doesn't practice corporal punishment. Well, you are *here* now, and you must abide by *my* rules. I'm sure you'll be happy with us.'

Old Victorian desks had been brought out of storage and packed into every available space in the classrooms. In Standard Four I was delighted to be allocated an upright single-seater which had an intricately-patterned cast-iron frame and an ink-stained wooden top, scarred by the knives of generations. I looked in vain for my paternal grandfather's name among the many inscriptions carved into the desk-lid. Then I remembered that he'd never been to school.

When everyone had settled in the headmaster entered to join Mrs Brownham, who was to be our teacher. Addressing her, but looking at *us*, he said loudly, 'Do not hesitate to send any offender straight to me.' They proceeded to have a quiet chat.

Then I spotted Annabel! She was sitting at one of the modern desks near the door and as far as I knew she hadn't been looking for me. I wondered if she guessed how I felt about her and if so did she care?

Opening my penknife I started to carve on the desk-lid in an unmarked spot between the inkwells. I'd got to 'G. Ll. loves . . .' before Mrs Brownham spotted me. 'Hm, I see,' she said, 'I didn't expect to see a vandal in Pengarth. It's the Headmaster's room for you, my lad!'

Eaglebeak listened attentively to the Brownham Report on Vandalism in the Classroom. 'Thank you, Mrs Brownham,' he said. 'You may now return to your class and leave this boy with me.'

Instead of walking over to his desk on which lay the dreaded cane, Eaglebeak, having noticed my stitches, took a few steps towards me and bent to have a closer look. He smelt of stale tobacco smoke.

'I don't know how you cut your lip, Llewellyn,' he said. 'But I *do* know that I shall not punish you today. I'm not a cruel man. But when your face is mended, I shall deal with you. Something to look forward to, don't you think?' He gave a little smile.

I was both surprised and relieved. 'Yes, sir,' I said.

Mrs Brownham answered my knock, let me in, and directed me to my desk, with a stern caution: 'Remember, now. More *carving*, more *caning*!'

'Yes, Miss,' I said, inwardly rejoicing at her ignorance of my escape.

*   *   *

An awful stench filled the classroom. Mr Pardoe the handyman was dipping strips of cotton mesh into a large tub of fish-glue and handing them up a ladder to his assistant for pasting onto the window panes.

'Very sticky, anti-bomb-blast tape,' he wheezed. 'Stop the flying glass, see.'

'Don't worry about the smell,' said Mrs Brownham, with a wry smile, 'it only lasts for a month or two. When our school at Elm Park was blown to bits every window remained in one piece!'

I was beginning to feel quite ill and longed to be out in the fresh air.

Mrs Brownham asked the pupils to introduce themselves in turn. At least this helped to take our minds off the foul smell. It was interesting to hear the strange accents and so many unfamiliar surnames. Many of the newcomers *looked* different, too, and several were fair-haired. But the first to speak had hair even darker than mine.

'My name is Michael Terenzi and I'm eleven. My father's Italian but I'm English.' His equally black-haired twin brother Denis followed.

The next had a mop of straw-coloured hair. 'My name is Albert Blenkinsop,' he said. 'I'm eleven too, but I'm all English.'

'I'm Tessa Thorneycroft . . .'

'Martin Greaves . . .'

'Peter Lawton . . . '

This is better than lessons, I thought, but I still felt pretty sick.

The roll-call continued, but now there were other distractions. The walls seemed to be closing in and I was sure an army lorry had just driven through the room. Michael Terenzi was singing in Italian and a detachment of the Home Guard was now marching past. Mr Pardoe was flicking lumps of dried fishbone glue at a squadron of miniature Messerschmitts buzzing around the ceiling. Mrs Brownham was holding a squeaking tortoise whilst Walter kept popping up and down shouting 'Bloody Belgians!'

All this seemed fairly normal . . . until a vision of heavenly loveliness weaved its way towards me through the motley throng. I felt sure I had met this beautiful girl once before – possibly in one of our old Celtic legends. She was bathed in a light that made her flowing white robe look like tailored snow and the intricate gold torque around her neck to glisten as she moved. Her long fair hair fell about her shoulders as she reached down to bring from beneath her feet a posy of exquisitely beautiful flowers of many colours. As she came near she glanced at me and smiled. And then she disappeared.

Chapter Five

The cold ends of the stethoscope felt pleasant against my chest. Dr Glennie was standing at my bedside assuring my mother that my recovery would be rapid.

'They say he was delirious before we collected him from the school,' said Mam, glancing at the doctor. 'Before you came he was talking all in riddles.'

'My, what a quaint way you Welsh have of putting things, Mrs Louellon,' said the doctor. She gave the thermometer a little shake and carefully placed it under my tongue. 'Talking all in riddles was he? What sort of things was he saying?'

'Well, as I was putting the hot-water bottle in his bed I'm sure he said, *"Odi'r crwban wedi cael ei fwyd eto"*? "Has the tortoise been fed yet?"'

'Interesting,' said Dr Glennie, 'but that's delirium for you. Shock can have strange after-effects.' She withdrew the thermometer. Checking it, she smiled and said that my temperature was nearly back to normal. 'I'll be back in a few days to remove those stitches.'

While my mother was seeing the doctor to the front door I found myself wondering what I might have been saying while I was delirious, hoping that whatever it was, it hadn't been too embarrassing.

My mother returned, looking quite beautiful in the sunshine that streamed through the window.

'Who's Annabel?' she said. I pretended I was asleep.

It was five o'clock when I heard the school bus enter the village. Soon my brother was in the house, and after briefly talking to my mother he came pounding up the steps and into the bed-room. He dropped his heavy satchel and came across to sit on my bed where I was propped up on pillows.

'*Shwd wyt ti, Ger?*' he said. 'How are you?'

'Never felt better,' I replied, and meant it.

Gareth held up three fingers, and in English, in the manner of a trainer speaking to a concussed footballer, said: 'How many digits?'

I wondered if the reason for his use of 'digits' was because he was taking Zoology at grammar school.

'*Dera 'mlaen!*' he said impatiently. 'Come on, how many?'

'*Cant a thrigain,*' I said. 'A hundred and sixty.'

'Mam!' shouted Gareth. 'He's getting better!'

That evening Walter arrived, bearing old copies of *The Champion* and *The Wizard*. Later I learned that to get the comics for me he had traded two full sets of cigarette-cards with an entrepreneurial evacuee. I knew how much he'd prized *Flags of the World* and *Animals of All Countries;* had I known then of his selfless exchange I would have thanked him properly.

I wasn't exactly yearning to go back to school, but I was missing the company of my peers. It wasn't a new feeling, for already I'd lost some schooling through minor illnesses. My brother was luckier. He rarely had an ache or a pain, although he did once have an attack of mumps.

After two days I was well enough to go out for a walk. The days were warm and the neighbours' gardens full of summer sounds. Nearby I could hear the *tish, tish, tish,* of Oli Pritchard's hoe picking its way between his lettuces. Three plots away the contents of Dic Morgan's lavatory bucket were being routinely applied to a clump of rhubarb which was already of Brobding-nagian proportions. In his ramshackle shed Twm the Poacher was feeding his obedient Welsh springer spaniels. Over to my right Jemima Jenkins was leaning over the wire mesh of her chicken run trying to catch one of the fowls, her obvious difficulty suggesting that the bird had recognised the knife she was holding.

The plots of the good gardeners weren't necessarily the tidiest. My uncle Gwyn, who lived two doors away, meticulously measured the distance between rows of carrots and parsnips and he would spread lime as if painting a picture. However, the yield from his garden was always meagre, whereas my father, who didn't claim to have green fingers, seemed to be able to throw a bucketful of peelings into a trench to produce a good crop of potatoes.

I enjoyed the one-upmanship arguments that gardeners would have at street corners on summer evenings. Some of their outrageous claims would rival those of anglers.

'I've got tomatoes so big you couldn't find a dinner plate to hold one. What about that, then?'

'Perhaps you're not feedin' 'em enough.'

'Mine are so delicious they taste like grapes, mun.'

'D' you think you'll ever get 'em to taste like tomatoes?'

I remember looking over Illtyd Probert's garden wall and seeing him admiring his magnificent runner beans.

Noticing me, the preacher raised his eyes to heaven and said, 'Aah, but there's only *one* Gardener, you know. Mind you,' he said, pointing to a large pile of manure at the bottom of the path. 'There's nothing wrong with giving Him a helping hand now and again.'

Before leaving the plots I took a good look to see how Shadrach Evans's *Golden Drop* gooseberries were coming along and promised myself a foray or two in a few weeks' time.

*   *   *

I winced as the stitches came out.

'And now, laddie, you'll be able to kiss the lassies again.'

I blushed hotly in contemplation of the horror of such an event with most of the girls I knew.

I returned to a school that seemed to have changed over the last three days. Most noticeably, at playtime the evacuees were less shy. The exceptions were the brothers Marks. Isaac and Jacob would sulk in a corner of the yard and reject all attempts to draw them into games. The younger of the two, already dubbed 'Harpo', was in my class and would often sit at his desk with his head resting on folded arms. We were soon to learn that in Standard V his brother 'Groucho' was behaving similarly.

Mr Pardoe and his assistant had finished pasting up all the windows and the smell had noticeably lessened. Even Mrs Brownham seemed different: she smiled frequently and I wondered why I hadn't liked her.

Annabel was almost totally hidden from me in class by the big Terenzi twins who shared a double desk. When I did get a glimpse of her she was usually intent on her work and I rarely caught her eye.

During breaks the girls played in their own yard which was separated from ours by a wall that had smooth rounded cap-stones. Climbing up for a forbidden peep into the girl's yard was to risk being caught by the ever-watchful Eaglebeak, for the wall was immediately below his office window. Nevertheless, on that first morning back, on the pretext of searching for a tennis ball that had been kicked over from our yard, I incautiously climbed onto the wall. Like an Indian scout scanning the prairie I soon spotted Morfydd Morgan holding the ball; she was standing in a group and dared me to go over to collect it.

'Come on, then. One kiss to get it back!' she said with a big grin.

Suddenly I knew I was on the spot as a number of boys had gathered behind me, hopeful of some drama. Morfydd was a bright and breezy but not particularly attractive fourteen-year-old who'd soon be leaving school to go into service at the local mansion Tŷ Mawr. Had Morfydd been Annabel I would have been over in a flash. However, in the circumstances I decided that there were more important things in life than tennis balls.

Then Annabel appeared. She took the ball from Morfydd and held it up, smiling and looking at me teasingly.

One of the other girls said, 'Come on down and get it, Geraint. Give her a kiss and she'll give you the ball.'

'Yes, come on Ger, what are you waiting for?' called out another.

The boys were listening to all this.

'For Christ sake, mun, *jump*!'

I jumped . . . and landed to see that Annabel had handed the ball back to Morfydd. Red with embarrassment I walked over to Morfydd and kissed her. The cheering and laughing from both sides of the wall brought Eaglebeak into the girls' yard.

'*Girls'* yard, eh?' he said. He was swinging his cane as he came over to me. Then he started on my legs.

Swish! 'That's for carving the desk.'

Swish! 'That's for climbing the wall.'

Swish! 'That's for being in the girls' yard.'

Then: *Swish!* . . . *Swish!* – for nothing in particular.

I knew I deserved some punishment and felt no real resentment; except perhaps for the tennis ball incident.

My legs were still stinging as I walked home from school amongst a small group.

'What was it like?' said Verdun Jones.

'The caning, you mean?' I said.

'No, mun, kissin' Morfydd Morgan!'

'She's a nice girl.'

'Yeah, but she's no Hedy bloody Lamarr!'

'And you are no Clark Gable, either! Boris Karloff, more like!'

'But it wasn't me who 'ad to kiss 'er, you daft bat!'

I was glad to be among friends. Who knows what enemies might have said? Not for the first time in my life Walter came to my rescue.

'I've been thinkin', Jones,' said Walter, 'Yew must 'ave been 'orrible when yew was a baby.' I guessed from past experience that he was pulling his opponent onto the punch.

'Fancy *you* sayin' 'at, you bloody bugger,' said Verdun. 'I bet when you was in your pram, you were so bloody ugly people used to cross over to the other side of the road to avoid lookin' at you. Ha-ha!'

'Very trew, very trew,' said Walter. 'But when *yew* was in *yewer* pram, people used to come over to take a look and then say to yewer mam: "Oh what a lovely pram, Mrs Jones!"'

'You can go to 'ell, 'Opkins,' said Verdun as he walked off.

'Right, Geraint, I want a word with yew in private,' said Walter.

We left the group and slipped into Pegler's Stores, by far the largest of Pengarth's retail outlets. Apart from Uncle Dai's greengrocery business the village had a post office that doubled as a newsagent's, two butcher's shops run by local farming families, and a house from which small ironmongery items could be obtained. Intriguingly there were also two or three households that supplied from meagre stock cigarettes, tobacco, and confectionery, 'after hours'. These had been licenced years before for the benefit of coalminers who often saw daylight only on Saturday afternoons. In a tiny window was a notice that never failed to cause a giggle: 'This establishment is closed on Sundays, Mondays, Tuesdays, Wednesdays, Thursdays, Fridays, and Saturday mornings'.

The three grocery shops in the village were quite different from each other. Siop Martha, near the Twyn, was where most of the Welsh speakers picked up their provisions and items of local news. My father's cousin, Bopa Martha, was a Mistress of the Gossip. She used the paraphernalia of her tiny shop as props and her theatrical gestures enhanced the credibility, colour, and the mischief of the story she happened to be telling. It was said that she sometimes gave discount if she felt a tale had gone well.

Siôn Williams's small shop on the Groeslon catered only for those with infinite patience, for he would take twenty minutes to make up an order that even Bopa Martha would have completed in five. However, Siôn couldn't be faulted on fairness and precision. One of our friends, a man not given to exaggeration, told us that he had once seen the grocer sawing a boiled sweet in half. It was also said of Siôn that when he was a lad he could peel an orange in his pocket.

Pegler's Stores was a cut above the others; an emporium where, in addition to groceries, many other items could be obtained: paraffin, rope, gardening tools, seeds, and so on. The store had changed hands several times since the prosperous days of the entrepreneurial Wyndham Evans, in whose time more than a dozen locals were employed delivering orders. But it was still a large shop for a small village.

Opposite the long counter sacks of barley, rolled oats, wheatgrain, and bran stood in a neat row. A further row of bags contained chicken corn, dog biscuits, and such like. An occupant of the shop was Wolf, a grossly overfed Alsatian who must have thought he was a hippopotamus. On a hot day after a shower of rain Wolf could often be seen out on the road lying in a pool of water. How he had summoned the energy to cross the road was a mystery to most; however, some of us knew his secret, for we had once seen Mr Smitherham wheeling him out of the shop on a sack-truck.

For our chat Walter and I sat on the floor, one on each side of the sleeping Alsatian.

'Yew bloody asked for that today, didn't yew!' whispered Walter,

'I suppose so,' I whispered back. 'Were you there, then?'

'Aye, I was there with the others by the wall, laughin' like 'ell. Couldn't 'elp it, see!'

'That's all right,' I said.

'Anyway,' said Walter, 'I know something that yew don't know and *should* know. So I'll tell yew.'

'Come on, then,' I said. 'What is it?' I was afraid it might be something involving Annabel.

Leaning across the snoring dog Walter whispered: 'It wasn't the noise that brought the Eagle out today, it was Dilwyn. I saw 'im creeping towards Eaglebeak's office. Next thing yewer legs were gettin' it!'

'So what,' I said. 'No more than I would expect from Dilwyn.'

'Do you'm really think the dawg be understanden what you'm a tellin' 'im, 'sno?' The Somerset brogue of Mr Smitherham, the store's general help was unmistakeable, as were his brown boots and tweed trousers. A leather apron was secured around the waist by a red necktie. One pocket of his waistcoat contained a row of well-sharpened pencils and an off-white, collarless flannel shirt was closed at the neck by a gold stud.

'You'm Trefor's lad, bain't ee?' said Mr S. 'You'm should'n be in 'ere, oiden fraam the sun – go laang wi ee.'

We left the shop, somewhat uncertain about what the Englishman had just said. 'The evacuees don't talk like that,' I said to Walter.

'No,' he agreed. 'But I don't understand most of what *those* buggers do say, either.'

'What do you think of them?' I said, as we reached our parting point.

'Think of who?' he said.

'The evacuees, mun.'

'Oh, them! They're OK, I s'pose.' That was high praise coming from Walter and from that moment I knew that he was in fact quite fond of them. And so was I.

'Meet yew later?' said Walter. 'We'll be seein' a lot of the vacs, I 'spect.'

'No. I've got Cubs this evening.'

'Tomorrow, then. Ta ra.'

I called at the post office shop and bought the latest *Champion* that contained a 'Rockfist Rogan RAF' serial. The previous week it really looked as if Rockfist had 'had it'. We had left him dangling upside down on a rope attached to one ankle and suspended from a parapet high up on the spire of Cologne Cathedral in the heart of Germany. From the cobbled yard below a dozen Nazi guns were trained on the swaying figure. A truck waited, engine running, ready to take his remains away. In his pocket was the object of his mission: a document upon which hung the fate of thousands, if not millions, of English people. This bit had always bothered some of us greatly, for we weren't sure where it left the Scots and the Welsh.

A good down-to-the-waist wash at the tub and then, with *The Champion* in hand, to the table for the meal we called tea, that some evacuees called supper. What we called supper was much later, near bedtime – often a fry-up of food left over from tea. Other evacuees called our tea 'dinner', which is the name we gave to the midday meal they called lunch. Lunch was what we called a packed snack to be consumed any time, but preferably in the morning. But I was relieved to find that breakfast was called 'breakfast'!

Gareth arrived from the school bus, joining me at the table for the beef pie that our mother had cooked using the whole week's ration of meat. Mam asked my brother the usual questions about his day at the grammar school and I contrived to read *The Champion* while enjoying my succulent pie.

I should have known Rockfist would escape uninjured. By the second mouthful he'd managed to swing towards the spire and attach himself to a gargoyle, at which point he unclamped the rope from his ankle. Two more mouthfuls and he had walked along a lip of masonry and squeezed himself in through an unglazed window, to find himself conveniently in a priests' robing room. Then it remained only to stir another piece of flaky pastry into the gravy to find that our hero had dressed himself in clerical vestments and had calmly made his way to the ground floor of the cathedral and out onto the square, past hordes of frantically searching members of the Wermacht and the Gestapo. As I wiped my plate dry with a slice of Betsi's bread, Rockfist was sizing up his chances of getting into the tiny aeroplane standing on the tarmac at a nearby Luftwaffe base. I would have to wait another week for the next miracle.

I had been in the Cubs for two years and would soon be gaining promotion to the Scouts, an event to which I was greatly looking forward. The move would allow me to wear those little green stocking-tabs and I would be able to carry a six-foot staff with measuring notches on it like the one Gareth had.

Cubs' meetings were held in the shed opposite the parish church. This was a small whitewashed stone building in which the parish magazine was printed on an ancient press. The old machine took up most of the available space and we had to tuck ourselves in wherever we could. Dai Robbins, Leighton

Howells, Billy Davies, and I, managed to squeeze our bottoms onto the little windowsill, while others were happy to sit cross-legged on the flagstoned floor.

Our Cubmaster the new curate Raymond Vaughan closed the door behind him and immediately launched into his address to the 'troops'.

'I have two main things to tell you tonight,' he said. 'Firstly, within a week or so, our pack will be expanding to include a number of evacuees, some of whom are already established Wolf Cubs.'

'Secondly,' he continued, 'next Saturday you'll be attending at the parish church what is being described as "The Wedding of the Year".'

Vera Morgan, arguably the most beautiful young lady in the village, would be marrying a young Polish Officer, a flying instructor at RAF St Athan down in the Vale of Glamorgan. Some said it had been a romance worthy of a Hollywood picture, and certainly Vera's looks were of film-star quality. Stanislav Lasczkowski had escaped to Britain at the outbreak of war and his flying expertise was put to immediate use. At the end of most training sessions he would sneak away to swoop low over Vera's house, dipping his wings when directly above it. Before leaving he would scatter messages in commendable copperplate on cards that had been lovingly decorated with tiny pictures of roses. These would flutter down to be gathered by boys who were more than eager to deliver them to the beautiful object of the airman's affection.

The wedding turned out to be a magnificent event. Goodwill towards the happy couple was almost palpable. The RAF was well represented, as were the other services. Scouts, Guides, Brownies, and Cubs were given pride of place up front where we enjoyed a clear view of the choir. Dilwyn Price-Davies was sitting at the end of the front row; I had forgotten that he was a chorister and the neatly combed hair and saintly expression contrasted strongly with my usual image of him.

The organ heralded the arrival of the bride on her father's arm. Farmers, miners, quarrymen, and office workers, many with ornately-hatted wives, feasted their eyes on a figure of utter loveliness as the bride glided down the aisle. The congregation murmured appreciatively and many a handkerchief was raised to a moist eye. The bride joined her husband-to-be who wore the powder-blue uniform of the Polish Air Force. Standing before the altar, the pair faced the august figure of the Reverend I. T. Bendigeidfran Jones, Vicar of this Parish.

All through the service my thoughts kept wandering: from fighter pilots to Dilwyn; from Vera to Annabel. I wondered if Annabel was in the church or in the crowd outside.

The ceremony followed the usual pattern, but the final blessing included a few Polish words that the versatile vicar had learned especially for the occasion. Stanislav smiled broadly and whispered a translation to his bride.

The service was concluded with a prayer in Welsh and hymn in English, during the singing of which the happy couple and their attendants proceeded to the vestry to sign the register.

'Love divine, all love excelling, joy from Heaven to Earth come down . . .'

The tune was *Blaen Wern*, but without the glorious four-part harmonies that would have been heard in a Welsh nonconformist chapel.

Dilwyn caught my eye and pretended not to see me. He affected the silly expressions adopted by some choirboys. I was counting the number of youngsters in the choir who had at some time fallen foul of their fellow chorister.

All heads turned as the smiling couple emerged from the vestry. The church door opened and the old pipe organ wheezed into the Wedding March. There would be no bell-ringing because that would have indicated an enemy invasion. A multi-coloured cloud of confetti met the couple as they came out of the church. There was much embracing and I noticed Vera's grandfather William Morgan talking animatedly to Stanislav and shaking his hand vigorously. I wondered how they were managing to communicate, for although the Pole spoke almost faultless English, Vera's grandfather knew hardly a word.

Following an age-old local custom, as the couple moved slowly down the path, a few shotguns were pointed to the sky and fired. At weddings in my grandfather's time they used a cannon made at the old Pengarth Ironworks. The practice was discontinued after a guest, while checking a suspected misfire, had blown his leg off.

The newly-weds were obliged to pass between two lines of six uniformed Polish airmen who, as they approached, raised ceremonial swords to form an arch of glinting steel. In accordance with local tradition, children had tied up the churchyard gate; only when the best man had thrown a fistful of pennies was it opened.

In the afternoon there were sports and games for children on the Dwrlyn fields, while the wedding party retired to the Church Hall for what was inexplicably called the Wedding Breakfast. At 7 p.m. an RAF car came to collect the couple, and Vera's parents watched tearfully as it left amid a clamour of good wishes.

Six months later the same faces would again be seen at St Catwg's, apart, that is, from Stanislav's. His plane had been shot down, and he was being buried on the north side of the church-yard in the shade of the big copper beeches.

Chapter Six

Beneath bluebell-coloured summer skies Pengarth was a handsome place. In autumn it had a special beauty as dying bracken turned the Garth hill bronze and mountainside streamlets sprang from crevices like threads of silver. In winter a shadow-filled landscape would often be transformed into a splendour of snow or hoarfrost. However, it was in summer that Pengarth truly blossomed. Here and there, from the beechwood on the Lesser Garth to the birches and oaks of Cwm Llwydrew, the greenery would be relieved by bursts of colour: foxgloves amongst fallen trees near the Ffynnon Gruffydd spring; flag-irises on the bank of Coed y Bedw brook; cowslips in a corner of *Cae Twm Tincer*, Tom the Tinker's Meadow. Amid the hedgerows red-berried hawthorn and mountain ash grew from grassy banks rich with violet columbine, campion, thistle, and knapweed. The war had determined that where sheep had grazed for centuries, golden wheat and barley now thrived; and at least half a dozen crofts were now producing main-crop potatoes.

Other changes were also noticeable. Clusters of sand-filled hessian bags, packed in tight rows one above the other, had long gripped many a town building in a mud-coloured embrace. Now our school, two or three shops, and a few private houses had them too. All military vehicles passing through the village were typically camouflaged with jigsaw puzzles of brown and green.

Rationing quickly became a way of life. It was frustrating for those of us old enough to remember the days of plenty. It was sad to see Uncle Dai moving about the village with only potatoes and swedes to sell, his cornucopian fruitcart now just a memory. White bread was soon to be replaced by a grey-brown variety, golden crunchy cornflakes by fragments of khaki cardboard. Most of our previously enjoyed pop drinks had disappeared, to be replaced by the ubiquitous *Tizer*. For long periods there would be no *Tizer* either; and for a time sweets and other confectionery would almost completely disappear from the shops.

However, wives and mothers worked wonders in their kitchens. My ingenious mother, with some valuable help from the wireless, would create culinary masterpieces from dried egg and dried milk.

Sugar was rationed to twelve ounces per person per week and I gave most of my portion to Mam for toffee-making. The four-ounce weekly allowance of butter would normally be just enough for a few rounds of toast. To the Welsh, a nation nurtured on pig meat, four ounces of bacon per person per week was a real challenge. Likewise, the recently imposed ration of an ounce of cheese was hardly enough to tempt a hungry mouse. Officially eggs were unrationed, but like many other items they found their way 'under the counter'. Each week we saved the cream from our milk to make butter. Gareth and I would take it in turns to shake the preserving jar until the butter separated. After removing the soft yellow mass from the container we would add salt before pressing out the superflous liquid through a muslin cloth. Finally we would shape the butter into a block by patting with a broad-bladed knife.

It was ironic to see commodities no longer available still being tantalisingly advertised, now with fading display material. In one of Pegler's windows a large card depicted children squabbling over possession of a bar of *Five Boys* chocolate and alongside it a cut-out of a black cat which reminded smokers of another product of the past. In their other window was a box which had once contained FIFTY FIREWORKS FOR

FAWKES NIGHT FUN AND FROLICS with illustrations of Roman candles, starbursts, Catherine wheels, and bangers, reminding us of more colourful and carefree times.

Although the shortages were felt by everyone, certain families were particularly hard hit. From time to time at Assembly the headmaster would solemnly read out the names of those who had died on active service. One had been a local rugby hero who, to our young minds, had been indestructible. An admirer of my father, with whom he shared an interest in literature, Iorwerth Rees was a frequent visitor to our house before he joined the Merchant Navy. They would exchange books and talk for hours about the works of the masters and it was strange to hear them analysing English writing while conversing mainly in Welsh. The names of Shakespeare, Shaw, Joyce, Huxley, and others were as familiar to me as if they lived in the next street, even though I had never read them. They would also discuss Welsh literature, in particular the poetry of Islwyn, whom they both considered to be a genius. Iorri, despite his bookishness, was as solid as rock on the rugby field, virtually unstoppable on the run, and a giant in defence. Now he was lying somewhere on the bed of the North Sea, unimaginably dead.

On the periphery of an industrial belt, Pengarth was used to life's uncertainties; we were continually reminded of the *true* price of coal-extraction and steel-making. However, our community tended not to accept tragedy with much stoicism; every loss was mourned deeply and openly. Those who had narrowly escaped death often bore scars that were the trademarks of a class that had little choice but to labour hard. At the top of our row of cottages there lived a man with one arm; at the bottom, a man with one eye.

I will never forget the day Twm the Poacher's son was brought home on a stretcher from the iron ore mine. I watched from the window as workmen carried the corpse to Twm's cottage. The old man came out, threw his arms around his dead son, and tearfully cried, *'Theo, Theo, mab annwyl, dera'n ôl i mi wnei di!'* 'O, Theo, dear son, come back to me!' But Theo had gone for ever. His head had been pulped.

There are those who would have argued that loss of life in defence of the realm is different. But a sense of honour or duty does little if anything to leaven grief. As soon as they heard the news about Iorri Rees my parents went to see his mother. She had been widowed by a rock fall at the quarry only two years previously and now a German submarine had deprived her of her only son. When Mam and Dad returned home that evening they were weeping. It was the only time I ever saw my father cry.

Several of the evacuees' families had suffered tragedies, but mostly they were reluctant to talk about them. The Terenzi twins' parents, officially classified 'aliens', had been cruelly imprisoned at the beginning of the war. Soon after their release Mr Terenzi was killed while on fire-watching duty during a raid on Chatham Docks.

As the weeks passed the evacuees settled comfortably into our way of life. We benefited from their town-bred attitudes and they enjoyed the rough and tumble of our rustic ways. Finding how different Wales was from their preconceptions greatly helped the absorption process.

Many evacuees were eager for more knowledge about what some called 'The Principality' – the land we call *Cymru* in Welsh and 'Wales' in English. I would have loved to talk to Annabel about such things but we seemed destined never to get together. Her brother, though, was very keen to learn about our history and he could have had no better teacher than Gareth, who had become a firm friend. One Saturday afternoon at the Twyn I listened-in to their conversation.

'So Wales isn't part of England, then?' said Ronnie.

Gareth smiled and said that it depended on how you looked at it. 'We prefer to call ourselves British,' he said. 'Just like the Scots and the Northern Irish we are part of *Britain*, not England.'

'But we are British, too,' said Ronnie with a frown.

'Yes, but the Welsh are the remnants of the *ancient* Britons. We once inhabited what is now called England as well as what is now called Wales. King Arthur was our great hero – he fought against your lot, the invading Saxons.'

'What about your lingo, then?' said Ronnie. 'We didn't know it existed till we came here!'

'Well, your teachers should have told you that the language of the ancient Britons has survived in Wales. Another branch is spoken in Brittany in France, but the Cornish version has almost died out.'

'How does your language differ from English, then?' asked Ronnie.

'English is a Germanic language, whereas Welsh is a Celtic tongue, a cousin of Irish and Scots Gaelic, and is vastly different from English.'

'And here,' said Ronnie, 'poets are considered heroes. In Chatham they'd be called cissies!'

'Yes, we have plenty of poets,' said Gareth. 'And they're definitely not cissies!'

'Hey, I've just realised,' said Ronnie, as if he had just discovered the meaning of life. 'Your language should be called "British" rather than Welsh!'

'Exactly!' said my brother. 'You might remember to tell them that when you get back home!'

'I promise,' said Ronnie.

I was about to go and look for Walter when Gareth looked at me archly and said to Ronnie: 'By the way, how's your sister, Ron?'

'Why do you ask?' said Ronnie.

'I think my brother would like to know, but he's too shy to ask.' I felt myself blushing, but said nothing.

'Well, she's quite happy really,' said Ronnie. 'The only thing is, she spends most of her time up on the farm playing with her friend – they're quite inseparable.'

'Oh, who's the friend?' said my brother.

Yes, who the hell is this friend? I thought miserably.

Ronnie kicked at a stone. 'Lightning, our tortoise,' he said. 'She insisted on bringing him. He's been with our family since my mother was young.'

It was a lovely day again. The sun was bright, the sky was blue, and the daisies were beautiful. Life was still wonderful.

I was about to leave the mound when I noticed that the Terenzi twins, to much acclaim, were showing off their latest wooden masterpiece. We had all admired their painting skills and also their immaculate handwriting, but now they were caught up in the latest craze. Everyone was carving model aeroplanes, sometimes with admirable results; however, the Terenzis were the masters. A Terenzi Spitfire or Messerschmitt would have been fashioned with nothing more sophisticated than a cobbler's knife.

Evacuee Bobby Townsend introduced us to the excitement of roller-skating and willingly lent his beloved possessions to anyone who wanted to learn to skate. However, it was only Walter who, despite his physical handicap, came anywhere Bobby's expertise. He told me that when he was skating, he felt 'bloody marvellous'.

I heard a familiar sound and turned to see Walter rolling past Pegler's shop. He coasted up the short hill to the Twyn mound and came to a stop in front of me.

'I've been looking for yew everywhere,' he said breathlessly, as he removed the skates. 'I've got to talk to yew. There's an alert on.'

'Alert' was a word that had quickly come into common use and meant only one thing.

'I didn't hear the warning,' I said, looking at the sky and seeing no sign of enemy aircraft.

'Not an air-raid this time,' said Walter. 'Let me take these skates back to Bobby across the road, and then I'll tell yew something that's a bloody big secret at the moment, innit.'

By the time he came back I was bursting with curiosity.

'So what's this big secret, then?' I said.

'Well, now,' said Walter, 'yew are the only one I'm tellin', see? Anyway, by tomorrow everybody will know.'

'For God's sake, *tell* me then!'

'The Marks Brothers have bloody gone missin'.'

'Oh. Pity,' I said. 'I *love* their films.'

'Very funny,' said Walter. 'I mean *our* Marks brothers, Groucho and Harpo!'

'Oh, I see,' I said. 'How do you know?'

'I was skatin' past Penuel chapel vestry an' could see a group of people the other side of the far graveyard wall. The copper was there. So was Eaglebeak an' a few others.'

'And?'

'Well it looked so interestin', I 'ad to find out what the buggers were talkin' about, didn't I? So I opened the gate and struggled across the graveyard. And that was no bloody joke, I can tell yew, what with my leg *and* the bloody skates!'

'What were they saying?'

'Well, I 'eard Mr Hughes – yew know, Mr Hughes of Bryn 'ouse, where the brothers 'ave been livin', sayin' they never came 'ome from school yesterday.'

'That's because they weren't in school yesterday!' I said. 'Nor the day before. I thought they must be ill.'

'No, they've buggered off,' said Walter. 'An' those people I saw were plannin' to go searchin' for 'em.'

'Why don't they alert everybody?'

'Cos if they're found this evenin', it won't look so bad for Eaglebeak.'

'It's not his fault,' I said.

'No, but it wouldn't look good, see. Anyway, if they don't catch 'em tonight, they'll get everybody out tomorrow, Scouts and all.'

'Do you think they'll find them?' I said, thinking it was going to be a terrible strain not telling Gareth about it.

'Who, Eaglebeak and his cronies? Never in a bloody month of Sundays.'

'I hope Groucho and Harpo are all right,' I said. 'I wonder where they are?'

'I've got more than a pretty good idea,' said Walter, 'but I'm not tellin' anybody. Not even yew for the time bein'.'

That stung a bit, but I was more concerned about the two boys and what could have happened to them.

I was in bed the following morning when I heard voices from downstairs and then the back-door latch clicking shut. I got to the window just in time to see Mr Evans the Scoutmaster get on his bike and hurry off.

By the time I got downstairs, Gareth was already in his Scout uniform, fixing the little green tabs onto his socks. Seeing me standing in my nightshirt he said, 'Mam will tell you all about it.'

Taking his staff from behind the door, he went out. I felt pleased that for once, I knew something before my brother.

'Ishta lawr 'machan i.' 'Sit down my boy,' said my mother, as she buttered me some toast. 'I have something serious to tell you.'

I decided not to admit that I knew what she was about to say.

'Two evacuee brothers are missing and search parties are being organised,' she said. 'The Scoutmaster's rushing about getting his troop together. Your father would have gone out with the Home Guard, but he had to go early to the quarry for an important interview. People are being excused chapel and church so they can take part.'

She put a plateful of toast before me. 'Everyone over twelve years of age, that is, so it'll be Sunday School for you as usual.'

'They weren't in school Thursday or Friday,' I said through a mouthful of toast. 'No-one really missed them.'

Said my mother, 'Mr Evans told me the headmaster and some of his friends went out looking for them last night. Nothing.'

I was almost tempted to repeat Walter's 'Never in a bloody month of Sundays.'

A week later the boys were still missing.

*　　*　　*

On a day too warm to be indoors Mrs Brownham was dragging us through the multiplication tables. We recited monotonously while she sat at her desk, yawning frequently. A wasp buzzed in and settled on her chin. She gave a yelp and brushed it away with the back of a hand. The wasp whizzed off like a Messerschmitt with Rockfist Rogan's Spitfire after it. This brought the exercise to a merciful close.

We then had a short history lesson, involving such admirable English stalwarts as Edward the First, who, in spite of the pain and misery he wreaked upon the Welsh, was implicitly conveyed as 'great and good'. Typically, never a mention of *Welsh* heroes. Not Mrs Brownham's fault, of course; our own teachers were just as negligent.

We were preparing to sing 'There'll Always Be an England', when a folded slip of paper found its way to me. For one exciting moment I thought it might have come from Annabel, but the untidy printing and the final 'W' immediately identified Walter: *'RAIVAL LAIN AT SIX. BE THERE. W.'*

Walter had taken a short cut through private gardens to save time. When I got to the lane he was fumbling for something in a tangle of brambles. He was cursing and swearing as he withdrew a brown paper carrier bag.

He licked his scratched hands. 'I should 'ave learnt my lesson this mornin', when I dumped this by 'ere on the way to school.'

'Can't blame the Belgians this time,' I said. 'Anyway, what's in it? The Crown Jewels?'

'Nah, the Crown Jewels wouldn't be worth a pound of pigs' pooh against what I've got by 'ere.'

I was losing my patience. 'Are you going to show me or not?' I said. 'Why are we here, anyway?'

Walter looked furtively up and down the lane before holding the bag open in front of me to reveal a loaf of bread and two bottles of milk.

'Let's 'urry,' he said. 'They'll be waitin' for us and I 'spect they're starvin'.'

'Who, for God's sake?' I said, as we moved off.

'Groucho and Harpo of course,' said Walter. 'I know where they are.'

'Hold on a minute,' I said. 'Don't you think you should tell somebody?'

'No, I bloody don't. And if yew aren't comin' with me, then bloody say so, innit?'

'Keep your hair on, Walter,' I said. 'Of course I'm coming.'

'Let's get a move on, then,' said Walter. 'We've got an 'ell of a long way to go.'

We kept going and, as ever, I was surprised at the speed with which Walter could cover ground.

We left the road, and keeping close to the hedges, wound our way through fields with ancient names that I translated for Walter: 'Red Rock'; 'Cuckoo's Well'; 'Crows' Tabernacle'. On the edge of Tom the Tinker's Meadow, where the trout-stream ran over smooth pebbles and little waterfalls gurgled into dark pools, we crossed into the birchwood. The softening and dampening of the ground by the innumerable springs that fed the Cwmllwydrew brook made walking difficult and my legs began to ache as we made for higher ground.

'Aren't there any footpaths?' I said.

'Yes,' said Walter, 'there are. But if we took the shortest route, sure as 'ell we'd bump into a search party.' I decided not to question the wisdom of Solomon Hopkins.

We left the wood at the top of a ridge where we stopped for a breather. Then, after much avoidance of bramble and nettle, we crossed a tricky stretch of wetland known as *Gwern y Cawr*, The Giant's Bog, to reach the foot of the big limestone escarpment on the Lesser Garth. During another short rest I found myself seriously thinking about what would be said when I eventually got home.

We scrambled somewhat painfully to the top of the plateau and proceeded through beechwood glades in the direction of the ancient iron ore mines. The area had many holes, some only a few feet across, others with twenty-five-yard-wide mouths. Beneath the ground there were caverns big enough to hold cathedrals. The Lesser Garth had been mined by the Romans, and in Elizabethan times the Pengarth Ironworks thrived upon the supply of readily accessible haematite. I thought of the often-heard story of how in Tudor times the local ironmaster Edmund Mathew was prevented by a Privy Council Order from selling cannons and other materials to the Spanish and shipping them out of Cardiff! I thought, too, with a slight shiver, of the *Ysbrydion*, the spirits that were said to dwell in the forest of the Lesser Garth.

At last we stopped and Walter signalled for me to be quiet. For a moment we stood in silence. Then Walter put his hands to his mouth and hooted like a tawny owl. After a few seconds a light appeared from a crevice in a rock wall a few yards away, transpiring to come from a candle in a jamjar held on a length of string. Harpo Marks emerged, followed by his brother.

'*Danke* for coming, Valter,' said Harpo. Then, raising the jamjar to get a better look at us: 'It is so good to see you both!'

'*Ja*,' said Groucho with a smile. 'Vould you like to see our living room?'

We followed Groucho and Harpo through a narrow tunnel for several yards until we came to a candle-lit chamber. Beneath a fissure in the rock serving as a chimney burned a wood fire over which water simmered in an iron saucepan. The air was heavy with the smell of cooking vegetables and wood-smoke. The brothers were using bracken for bedding and orange boxes for seats and a table. Enamel mugs stood on a rock shelf, and, surprisingly, tea-towels hung on a line of string.

'So what's happened?' I said. 'What are you doing here?'

'Ve'd had enough of being bullied at Bryn House,' said Groucho. 'Mrs Hughes vas nice, but Mr Hughes used to hit us and call us Jewboys. Ve couldn't take any more. *Nicht wahr?* Ve told Valter about it and he promised to help us. So here ve are. Until ve can go back to Chatham or to another house in Pengarth. To a *nice* family, *ja*?'

With the milk Walter had brought we made hot sweet tea. On one of the orange boxes could be seen the words Clarke Bros, Wholesale Fruiterers, West Canal Wharf, Cardiff; I recalled wistfully I'd seen that address many times on Uncle Dai's fruit-crates in the days of plenty.

I learned of the brothers' origins in Germany whence they'd escaped, tragically leaving their parents behind. After a short stay in a London children's home they had been sent to live with foster parents in Chatham. My feelings of sympathy for the Marks brothers gave way to apprehensive thoughts of what my own parents would be thinking. However, I realised that what I was going through was nothing compared with what the Marks brothers had experienced. I felt that had my parents known where I was and what I was doing they would understand.

During our conversation it became clear to me that Walter had been responsible for finding and furnishing the brothers' new home, not to mention the supply of food and drink. I wondered if he was going to be punished for all this; and if so, would I be an accomplice?

The brothers spoke of their childhood; of seeing their grandfather's shop ransacked; of whole families being taken away, never to be seen again. They were the only Jews I'd ever seen and I couldn't help wondering what Jesus had looked like.

Suddenly Walter got up and said to my great relief that it was time for us to go. 'It's not *me*,' he said, 'but Geraint's Mam and Dad will be worryin' their 'eads off.' The brothers nodded.

'So long for now,' said Walter.

'Nos da, bechgyn,' I said.

'Ah, that's Velsh, *ja?*' said Groucho. 'Perhaps I vill learn it vun day. Anyvay, *nos da*, Gerunt.'

We heard voices as we entered the birchwood and I recognised my father's among them.

'Promise yew'll say nothin',' said Walter as they came nearer.

'What do you mean?' I said.

'For Christ's sake don't tell 'em where the Marksies are!'

'It'll be difficult,' I said. 'But I'll do my best.'

'Right,' said Walter, and he disappeared.

'*Diolch i Dduw!*' – 'Thank God!' said my father, holding me tight.

'Where on earth have you been?'

'I went for a walk and got lost,' I said.

The look of relief on my mother's face as we entered the house was indescribable. After a long hug, she said that she'd never been so worried in all her life. She made me promise in future always to tell her where I was going, or at least where I was likely to be going.

After wolfing down an exceptionally late supper of poached egg on toast and cold rice pudding I was more than ready for bed.

'Don't wake Gareth, now,' said Mam, as I went upstairs. 'He's been out looking for you, too. Oh, by the way,' she called after me, 'you won't forget to say a prayer for those two missing boys, will you?'

Chapter Seven

Five days later the the Marks brothers gave themselves up after having heard from Walter that Eaglebeak of all people had agreed to take them in until a new home could be found.

It was generally believed that I alone had engineered the rehabilitation of the brothers. Try as I may I couldn't seem to get it across that it was Walter who had been responsible for caring for the boys during their absence. So much for human nature.

I have often thought that what I learned from Walter has been more important to me than much of what I learned at school.

One day during the summer holidays he accused me of being too precious.

'Geraint,' he said, 'yew make me bloody sick, mun!'

'I'm sorry you feel like that,' I said. 'But why?'

'There yew go again!'

'What d'you mean,' I said.

'Sometimes yew're just too goody-goody, mun. I mean – yew don't even bloody swear!'

'Yes, I do!'

'No, yew bloody don't!'

'Yes, I bloody *do*!' I shouted.

'That's more like it!' said Walter, laughing. 'See yew later,' he said, as he turned for home down the quarry lane.

Mam was radiant when I got home. A food parcel had arrived from one of her cousins in Pennsylvania. As we gazed wide-eyed at a range of confectionery that reminded us of better times my mother made it clear that a few friends and neighbours would also be sharing the contents.

After she had tucked the parcel away in the *cwtch* under the stairs, Mam said that she had something very important to tell me. 'On second thoughts,' she said, 'I'll wait till Gareth comes home and you can hear the news together.'

No amount of cajoling could persuade my mother to change her mind, but she did admit that it was very good news indeed.

I had no idea where Gareth was. He'd begun his school summer holidays a week before and he could have been anywhere. I went out several times to see if he was coming down the lane, but there was no sign of him. My mother made chips to go with some of the tinned Spam from the food parcel.

When Gareth eventually arrived he explained that he'd been boxing. He was good at sparring and he was strong and quick. When he said he'd been boxing at Nant yr Arian I felt my heart miss a beat.

In his youth Ianto Protheroe had been a formidable bruiser. An Army middleweight champion during the First World War, he'd been delighted to learn of Ronnie Webb's interest in the noble art, willingly clearing part of one of his big sheds to accommodate a ring. It was there that Gareth and Ronnie, who were of the same weight and build, had been sparring that afternoon.

'Was Annabel around?' I said.

Gareth looked up from his Spam and chips. 'Oh yes, she was,' he said. 'And the tortoise. Why don't you come with me next time?'

'Good idea,' I said, trying my best to sound casual. 'Let me know when you're going again.'

Then I remembered my mother's 'good news'. I dragged her out of the pantry.

'*Gwêdthoni Mam, gwêdthoni!*' I pleaded. 'Tell us, Mam, tell us!'

'Well,' she said, 'we've had a parcel from cousin Gwyneth in America.'

'Don't tease us, Mam,' I said. 'I've told Gareth about the parcel.' What was the *other* thing?'

She sat down. 'Your father is going to have to give up his job at the quarry.'

Gareth looked alarmed.

Continued my mother 'They've made him Assistant Manager!'

'*Bendigedig!*' cried Gareth. 'Wonderful! Wonderful!'

'That's marvellous, Mam!' I said.

'Yes, isn't it?' she said. 'He'll *double* his wages, you know! We'll be able to go away on holiday and visit Aunty Olive in Bristol. I've never been to England. Perhaps we can move to a house with running water and an indoor lavatory, electric light, and a cooker you switch on and off. And a vacuum cleaner like the one I saw in Tŷ Mawr house. And other important things, too . . . that is, of course, if . . .'

That reminded us that it was Friday, our father's worst boozing night. Another late homecoming, the personality change, the incessant talking into the small hours. Our mother's distress.

Then we had a real surprise. Dad walked in. Sober. Mam looked at him in disbelief as it was still early evening. '*Wyt ti'n sefyll?*' she said. 'Are you staying in?'

Dad was looking at us as he put his arms around Mam and said, 'Yes'. 'I'm going to give it a try.'

The following morning Gareth and I went to Twm the Poacher's cottage for our monthly haircut. We sat on a settle and waited for Twm, who had shuffled off to another room to get his barbering tools. He was singing an old Glamorgan song about the unrequited love of a poor thatcher for a rich farmer's daughter. The song was punctuated by the cough he'd had for as long as I could remember. It was loud, rasping, and rather scary; the cough, that is, not his singing, which was melodious enough. Two sporting guns adorned the wall above a large clock on the mantelpiece. Megan, Twm's spaniel, lay sleeping on a straw mat, doubtless dreaming of rabbits and pheasants. Pictures of woodcock and partridge hung on the wall each side of a Welsh dresser.

We liked going to Twm's. Not for the rather painful haircut; nor indeed for the glass of parsnip wine he sometimes gave us for an 'anaesthetic', but for the interesting things we learnt from him. He had few English words and they were almost unrecognizable to us. Oddly, he often used these when talking harshly to his dogs.

When he returned with his torture kit laid out neatly on a tray, he gave the spaniel a kick and demanded that she 'Grout! Grout!' Placing the tray on a small table he waved me onto a chair and put a towel around my neck. Then, as always, he gripped each ear firmly between finger and thumb and said: *'Ti isha 'rhein?'* 'Do you need these?' The burst of laughter that followed inevitably became a fit of coughing. Ritual over, he started on the serious business of trying to remove my ears.

Another thing that used to intrigue us about Twm was his frequent conversation with an invisible companion. 'Idris' would be asked to shut the back door, fetch a jack of water or put some more coal on the fire. We never saw a door shutting of its own accord, nor coal moving through the air. However, one day when Twm asked Idris to sit beside me on the settle, I felt very uneasy.

Pinch. Snip-snip. Tug. Snip-snip. Off would come hair and tiny flakes of skin as the old man worked the clippers around my head.

Gareth took his turn on the chair and asked Twm about the origin of the name of a nearby farm, Llwynybrain. Twm delivered a colourful explanation in Welsh but little is lost in the English translation:

'At Llwynybrain, The Grove of the Crows,' said Twm, 'a servant boy had been employed to keep birds away from the corn with a blunderbuss loaded with nails that pierced the birds' legs and pinned them to the branches of a tree. There was a great commotion and flapping of wings as the birds rose and wrenched the tree from the ground, flying off and eventually landing in a Herefordshire field where some brown cows were grazing. The animals were so frightened that their faces turned white. And that's how we got a new breed of cattle – the white-faced Hereford!'

*   *   *

My eleventh birthday came early in the summer holidays and Mam insisted that I had a party. At first I was against the idea: jelly, blancmange, etc., were for the very young, surely. After all, at the end of the year I'd be going to the grammar school.

However, my stance would soon change. My mother said that my pals would be disappointed if we didn't have a party. 'Some of Gareth's friends could come along too,' she said. 'Like that nice Ronnie.'

'And his sister,' said Gareth, looking up from *The Scout's Handbook of Survival* with which he was preparing for summer camp.

For my birthday my father bought me *Treasure Island*, a book I was to read avidly from beginning to end without putting down. It made me feel that I would have liked to live in the eighteenth century when doubtless I would have been a sailor on the southern seas. Recalling that I'd once been sick in a row-ing boat on Cardiff's Roath Park Lake did nothing to change my mind.

The party went well. Several neighbours and relations had helped my mother with sandwiches, cakes, and fruit. Ronnie and Annabel had brought theirs from the Protheroes, together with a large pot of honey. Bopa Meia's huge tray of cold rice pudding had been a great success, its popularity only slightly shaded by the bread pudding my mother had made using sultanas from Pennsylvania.

My father, sober as a deacon, contributed a hilarious mono-logue about an organ grinder and his mischievous monkey. Afterwards he shared a couple of humorous duets with Mr Smitherham who'd brought his ukelele, and by the time the latter had added a few George Formby numbers, it was time for everyone to go home.

I had been dying to have a long chat with Annabel, but alas, it wasn't to be. No sooner had she begun to tell me about how much she liked living with the Protheroes than my mother whisked her away to show her the kinds of things she thought a girl would be interested in. I'm sure Mam had always wanted a daughter. Embroidery work came out of one drawer, lacework from another. From yet another my grandmother's crocheted tablecloth, 'too precious to be used'.

I longed to have Annabel to myself, if only for a few minutes. To tell her how I felt about her and how I wanted to see more of her. To take her for walks in Coed y Bedw and perhaps recite to her a certain love poem I had learned. But all that would have to wait.

The party guests were leaving and Ianto Protheroe's cart was in the lane ready to collect Ronnie and Annabel. The farmer had come into the house and was talking to my father about the boxing arena he'd set up.

'They're an even match, those two,' he said, pointing at Ronnie and my brother with his huge pipe held pistol-fashion. 'Good timing and sharp footwork, both of 'em. I reckon they could make it in the fight game.'

'Well, with our boy at least,' said my father, nodding towards a fading photo on the wall, 'it's in the blood.' My father's first cousin Twmos Lee Llewellyn had been a mountain fighter at the turn of the century, long after bare-knuckle fighting had been made illegal. He was immensely strong and skilful and had won bets for many locals. Respected by all, he was also loved by the women of the village, many of whom when in their dotage still talked of his good looks and his gentlemanly manners.

'Did you ever see my cousin fight, Ianto?' said Dad.

'See him fight, indeed! Wasn't I with him that night we went to Cardiff after the rugby and got to Tiger Bay just in time to see Tali Evans, Wil Penmynydd, and Ithel Jones being thrown out of *The House of Blazes*?'

He went on: 'They'd been given a real going over by half-a-dozen foreign sailors. I can see Tali now. He came out through the window feet first, keeping his bowler on with one hand and holding his umbrella with the other! Then Wil and Ithel were thrown out, one after the other! The boys had been speaking Welsh, see, and Bonzo the landlord had taken exception to it even though there were Germans, Dutch, Somalis, and Chinese in there, all talking their own lingos. In a flash little Tali had got big Bonzo in an arm-lock. Oh dear, hullabaloo it was then, see, because up jumps these foreigners to the aid of the landlord, and although our boys put up a good fight they were no match for the Dutchies and the rest, who gave 'em a real pasting.'

We listened spellbound to the story that had been told in English until the excitement of recollection caused the teller to slip into the language in which he was more fluent. Gareth whispered a translation for Ronnie's benefit.

'So then what?' said my father, who'd probably heard the tale before, but clearly wanted us to have it straight from the horse's mouth.

'Well, we picked the lads up, brushed 'em down, and told 'em to make their way to Queen Street railway station. Then we went in and ordered a couple of pints. Twmos gave me a nudge and turned so that he had his back to the bar. Oh, *drampo, drampo*, I shall never forget it as long as I live!'

Ianto patted his pockets and there followed a ritual of pipe-filling, lighting with a paper spill, and much sucking and blowing.

We could guess what was coming, but were impatient for the details.

'He was a clean fighter, was Twmos,' said Ianto, at last. 'Never threw the first punch.' His pipe had gone out and he reached for another spill.

'So, Mr Protheroe,' I said, 'What did Twmos do *next*?'

My father gave me a sharp look.

'Sorry, Mr Protheroe,' I said. 'But I'm just dying to know!'

After a couple more puffs, Ianto put his pipe down on the hob and I knew that he was approaching the climax.

'Twmos started in English straight away, see, and said in a firm, steady voice: "I am Welsh and proud of it, and I will fight to the death for my right to speak in my own country the language in which my mother raised me. If anyone here wishes to dispute this right, let him be warned that I fear no man."

'Then, to me, in Welsh, "You look after the Chinaman, laddie, but watch out for his knife. I'll take the big 'un with the beard. I think he'll make the first move." At this point Bonzo gave a nod to the room. The Dutch sailor shot out of his chair and went for Twmos. Twm hit him on the chin and in no time flat the Dutchman was on his back, dreaming of tulips and windmills. Then it was a right free-for-all. Twm was immaculate. Bodies hit the floor one after the other. And stayed there.'

'What about the Chinaman, Mr Protheroe?' said Ronnie.

'Chinaman? What Chinaman?'

'You know, the one Thomas warned you to keep your eye on – the one with the knife.'

'Oh *him*?' said Mr Protheroe. Blowing on his knuckles, he said, 'I sent him to sleep with the nicest right cross I ever threw. He was lying there when we left, smiling like a baby. As for Bonzo, he was unconscious behind the bar. Twm had taken care of him, too.'

I could see Ronnie was very impressed.

As the farmer was lighting up again he seemed to be preparing to tell us more.

'And then there was that time in the Irish quarter,' he went on. 'In that pub in Mary Ann Street called *The Lakes of Killarney* . . .'

'Why don't you stop this silly old talk about fighting?' said my mother, who had just entered the room with Annabel. 'And you, Ianto Protheroe, a deacon at Bronllwyn, too!'

'Now, Ceinwen,' said Protheroe, you don't want your boys to grow up to be cissies, do you? Mind you, after seeing your eldest perform I don't think you have any worries there. I don't know about *this* one, though,' he said, reaching over to gauge the thickness of my arm. 'He wants a bit of feeding-up. Send him over to Nant yr Arian and we'll build him up with plenty of bacon and eggs!'

'No good arguing with you, Ianto Protheroe,' said my mother. 'You've always been the same – an answer for everything.' She gave the farmer a friendly push on the shoulder.

'Well, maybe,' he said, with a smile. 'Anyway it's time to go. My cows will be bursting.'

He threw a playful punch at Gareth as he went out, raising his other hand as if to parry a return. Ronnie and Annabel thanked my parents and followed him to the lane.

Before getting into the cart Annabel turned to me and said, 'I'm so glad the stitch marks have cleared up.'

'*Diolch*,' I said, 'I am, too.' Hardly a romantic exchange, but it had to suffice for the time being.

The farmer told the mare to 'geddup', and we said our good-byes as the cart moved away.

Oh, well, I thought. There'll be other times . . .

Chapter Eight

Pengarth baked in the summer sun. The normally verdant banks of Maesglas lane that snaked its way towards Nant yr Arian were now mostly brown.

As I walked up the ancient cart-track I could hear rumbling and clunking from across the valley behind me. At Uncle Gwilym's farm someone had obviously managed to get the hired steam traction-engine working and they were pumping water from Cwmllwydrew brook to save the late potato crop. Several volunteers had gone over to help, including my father and my brother. I felt a twinge of guilt for not being there, but I'd made a decision and would stick with it. Besides, I was a regular helper at Caerwen and I knew my uncle wouldn't mind me not being there for once.

I slowed down, wondering if I was doing the right thing. Will I be welcome at Nant yr Arian? What will I say if Annabel comes to the door?

I arrived at the kissing gate where the path left Maesglas cart-track, pointing the way to Nant yr Arian by way of the high field where Walter and I had abandoned our first expedition. The green of the gate stood out against the brown of the caked earth.

I asked myself over and over again if this was the 'point of no return'.

As I stood swinging the gate to and fro its squeaking hinges seemed to mock me. Then I remembered that although the gate was thought by locals to have the 'power of blessing' for young lovers it had probably also been the scene of many a solemn promise destined to be broken; but I wondered how many young couples down the ages had met at this place of tryst and troth subsequently to benefit from its influence. It seemed to me that the gate was a fitting place for momentous decision-making.

'Bugger it,' I said to myself, 'I'm going back home!'

I would never lose my affection for August, that glorious school-free month in which we tanned berry-brown and basked in the warmth of settled friendships.

Despite the enervating heat boys and girls of all ages played thirty-a-side games on Clawdd Siôn field; but it wasn't all fun for the cricket outfielders who slithered through cow-pats and were obliged to go home 'smelling of the country'.

The evacuees were intrigued by our game of Bomparino and they quickly became keen participants. Elsewhere it was known as 'Strong horses, weak donkeys', but we preferred the more exotic name. Two teams of six were selected and the leader of one group would brace himself against the wall with out-stretched arms. The others of his team formed up behind him, each bent over with his head between the legs of the one in front. When a solid 'back' was formed, members of the other side, on the sound of a whistle, would leap onto it one at a time and shuffle forwards in an attempt to collapse the 'horse'. A fixed period of time was allocated and some physical violence was allowed. It was deemed a poor contest if, upon its con-clusion, no one went home dented or bruised.

Every few weeks I would go to Caerwen to do odd jobs for my uncle. Walter usually came with me, for he loved the farm and everything to do with it.

I was very fond of Uncle Gwilym. He was tall for a Welshman, with broad shoulders, square chin, and ginger side-whiskers. He had a rather fearsome appearance, but his customary glaring expression belied mild manners and generosity. He may not have had my father's intellect, but in his own way he was very bright and whenever time and duty permitted, a keen student of local history. His wife, my Bopa Mari, was a melancholy soul dedicated to sharing her misfortunes with the world: aching joints, throbbing headaches, and a host of other miseries. A dark cloud of wretchedness seemed to hang over her. Walter had quickly spotted her deceitfulness.

'The woman's a pain in the arse,' he said early one morning as we crossed the yard with our buckets of pigswill. 'If I was yewer uncle I'd feed her to the pigs.'

'What, and poison them?' I said. 'What would he do then?'

As we leaned over the pens to fill the troughs the pigs made a great fuss. They seemed to recognise Walter and I found myself becoming less nervous of them. However, Uncle Gwilym had strongly advised against entering the pens, especially that of Boadacea, the old sow; who on one occasion had attacked a War Agricultural Committee inspector who was lucky to have escaped serious injury. Boadacea had missed her target and her teeth had become so firmly embedded in a wooden fence-post that it required three men and a tranquilising injection from a vet before the old pig could be freed. But Walter and Boadacea were such good friends that she would actually allow him to sit on her back while she fed.

Uncle Gwilym's other brood sow was Helen of Troy. She was lying down as eleven squeaking piglets fought to get to her teats. An undersized twelfth lay nearby on the straw and seemed to be fighting for breath. Helen had already devoured two of her litter and might have easily decided to see off the runt as well.

'She's going to eat that poor little bugger if we don't do something about it,' said Walter. With that he was over the wall, into the pen, scooping up the sick piglet, and climbing back to immediately start massaging its heart.

'Get some milk. Quick,' said Walter. 'Fetch the feeder.'

Seeing me hesitate he shouted: 'Get the bloody milk, mun, or this little 'un will die as sure as eggs!'

I shot off to the dairy where several sterilised feeders would be lying on a slate slab. Normally kept for motherless lambs and calves, one of them now with any luck would save the life of a sick piglet. From a nearby churn I quickly ladled some milk into a feeder and hurried back.

'Well done, Ger,' said Walter. 'That was pretty bloody quick.'

I offered to do some massaging, but Walter would have none of it. Soon he stopped what he was doing and, with one hand holding the little body to his ear, with the other he tapped the wall in time with the heartbeats.

'It's steady now!' he cried. 'Let's try 'im with the milk.' Walter placed the teat of the feeder into the little creature's mouth. For a few seconds nothing happened; then with a bit of a slurp and splutter the piglet started to drink eagerly. I could have sworn it was smiling.

''E's goin' to make it,' said Walter. 'I'm sure of it.'

I was now more than ever convinced that Walter was some sort of genius.

The feeder was only half empty before the piglet began to kick vigorously. Walter then leant over the fence and carefully released the little animal. Squeaking loudly, it dashed to join its siblings at the refectory. When it was happily sucking away Walter turned to me and said, 'Right, then, what's the next soddin' job?'

'Don't know,' I said. 'I'll think about it.'

I wanted to tell Uncle Gwilym what Walter had just done, but I knew he'd already left for the mountain to check his flock. In any case I knew that expressions of thanks would only embarrass my friend.

In fact the next job turned out to be a favourite one; never a chore, for I had a great fondness for horses. However, taking my uncle's working cob to the blacksmith had its problems, for the animal never wanted to go. But the return journey was always a pleasure.

A lot of the animals had names from Wales's colourful past. Owain Glyndŵr now had four legs and a bobbed tail. Some of his characteristics indeed recalled those of the great prince, but occasionally he could be as stubborn as a mule.

Our main problem was catching him. No sooner would he hear our voices than he would gallop off to a far corner of the field. However, this time Uncle Gwil had made it easy for us. My aunt spotted us as we crossed the farmyard and she had ached her way out of the house to tell us that my uncle had put the cob in the stable ready for collection. I knew it wouldn't be that easy but we thanked her before she moaned her way back indoors.

'I bet she's doing bloody cartwheels now,' said Walter.

'Well, maybe she really does have pains sometimes,' I said.

'Nah, yewer aunty's too bloody mean to 'ave pains,' said Walter.

Owain Glyndŵr recognised me as soon as I opened the top of the stable door and clearly connecting me with a trip to the smithy he immediately registered his disapproval by snorting and whinnying. He showed the whites of his eyes and reared repeatedly, the stable reverberating to the sound of his hooves pounding the door. I wondered what Gary Cooper would have done in such a situation. For once Walter was no help. He was wetting himself laughing.

Eventually he said, 'Remind me, how many 'orses 'ave yewer uncle got?'

'Just one other,' I replied. 'You know the one, the roan mare. She was shod last week.'

'Where is she now?'

'On *Cae Twm Tincer* I should think. But it's a big field, mind.'

'Can she be caught easy, like?'

'No trouble,' I said. 'But what are you thinking?'

'Yew'll see. I've got a plan. Just bloody go and bring 'er down by 'ere.

Twenty minutes later I led The Princess Nest into the yard and noticed that Owain G had become silent. Walter had put a halter on a fully compliant cob and was now leading him out to join The Princess.

'You know that we'll have to take both of 'em to the smithy, now?' I said.

'Course I bloody do!' he said. 'That's the plan, yew silly bugger. Can yew think of a better one?'

'Course not,' I said. 'You're a clever sod, Walter.'

The journey to the village, while predictably slow, proved to be relatively uneventful. However, now and again Owain G, the second in line, would show signs of his old reluctance by occasionally stopping to graze, thereby bringing the procession to a halt.

Walter was a model of patience; until he got in the way of one of Owain's bowel movements.

'Shit!' cried Walter. 'Stop for a minute. I've got to clean myself up.'

Having done the necessary to make himself respectable, he said as we moved off: 'Geraint, why do they sometimes call Wil Refail, *Wil y Gof*?'

'Because his name is William and *gof* is Welsh for black-smith.'

'What's that "raival" then?'

'It's *yr efail,* which means forge, or smithy. It comes from *gefail,* only you drop the 'g'.'

'What's Wil's real name, then?'

'Mathews,' I said.

Walter made a face. 'Yew've bloody lost me, now,' he said. But he wasn't giving up.

''Orse shoe, then. What do yew say for 'orse shoe?'

'*Pedol* is a horseshoe, *pedoli* is shoeing.'

'OK, what about 'orseshit, then,' said Walter. 'What's 'orse-shit in the language of 'eaven?'

'*Tail*', I said, carefully saying 'taa-eel' for his benefit.

'Same smell in both bloody languages,' said Walter, by now himself smelling only slightly of horse manure. He stroked his charge's neck and said, 'Yew wouldn't be a bloody Belgian 'orse by any chance, would yew?'

We reached our destination and presented Owain to the blacksmith. Strangely, the horse always behaved well after arrival; it was as if he had made his point and was now resigned to letting the work be done so that he could be homeward bound as soon as possible.

He stood calmly as I tethered him by the halter to an iron ring fixed in the white-limed wall. Wil always provided hay for his clients and soon Owain was munching contentedly. Outside, Princess Nest was tied by a long rope to a gate, cropping from the lush grass verge. Walter had gone for a stroll, leaving me to chat with my interesting old friend William Jefferson Mathews, otherwise W*il Refail, Wil y Gof,* the blacksmith who was also a wordsmith.

I stroked Owain's nose as his old worn shoes were removed.

'You look just like your grandfather did fifty years ago,' said Wil. 'Do you take after him? I'm sure you steal apples and

97

knock on doors like he did. *Wyt ti'n hela?*' ('Do you hunt?')
And then, before I could answer, *Cadnoid? Merched?* ('Foxes?
Girls?') Your grandfather knew how to take care of himself, too.
I expect you have a scrap now and again, don't you?'

I was about to get a word in when he continued: 'What
about verse? Do you write verse?'

I could see that Wil didn't really want answers.

The furnace hissed and spat as the blacksmith's assistant
Clem applied the bellows. With one of the horse's legs bent
between his knees, Wil rasped away at the overgrown hoof. He
then repeated the procedure with the other three.

A short steel bar, glowing white hot, was deftly taken with
tongs from the furnace and swung onto the anvil. Wil then got
to work with the hammer. I watched fascinated as the smith
worked the hot metal, his muscles rippling as he rythmically
beat the shoe into shape.

The thudding sounds of the hammer on the metal contrasted
pleasantly with the alternate ringing strikes upon the anvil.

Each shoe had to be repeatedly returned to the furnace prior
to the first fitting. Then, after a lovely smell of burning hoof,
the shoe would be heated once more before being punched
with seven holes. After quenching in a tub of cold water it
would be nailed into place.

When Owain's hooves were painted with what looked like
creosote he looked really smart. I patted his neck and said,
'There you are, it's never as bad as you expect.'

Walter returned and Wil made some tea for us. I noticed that
as he was boiling the water and fetching milk and sugar he
would occasionally close his eyes and mutter a few words in
Welsh. I guessed what was coming.

Wil was a master of the *englyn*, a four-line stanza that must
obey complex rules involving internal alliteration, which at the
time was beyond my understanding. Country poets could com-

pose these pithy verses at the drop of a hat. We sat with our mugs of tea as Wil recited. The theme was Owain Glyndŵr arriving like a reluctant tortoise but leaving like an eager hare. Walter asked me to translate, but I made my usual excuse, namely that it doesn't sound so good in English; hoping that would suffice. But perhaps Walter knew me better than I knew myself.

'Trewth is yew couldn't bloody understand it, could yew!'

We rode the horses home bareback with Walter again in charge of Princess Nest. Like me, he was well used to riding without a saddle and with only a halter to steer. Owain knew the way home and would hold a fast trot. This time he went like Pegasus and I managed to get a fair grip with my knees around his barrel-belly. Walter despite his game leg did very well on the Princess.

In the village we passed a detachment of the National Fire Service having a practice session at the Twyn mound. Oddly, there were no youngsters about. We looked over into Clawdd Siôn field, but saw no-one there either.

Uncle Gwilym was holding the gate open for us as we arrived at Caerwen.

'That's enough for one day,' he said, taking charge of the horses after we'd dismounted. From his waistcoat pocket he took a couple of half-crowns and gave us one each.

'Diolch,' I said, and was surprised to hear Walter use the same word.

'Diolch, Mr Llewellyn,' he said. 'Yew are very kind.'

As my uncle took the horses away he said, 'There's something waiting for you both on the kitchen table.'

The refreshing coolness in the farmhouse was of the kind that exists only in ancient stone buildings with three-foot-thick walls. 'Y gegin', 'the kitchen', at Caerwen was in fact the large main living room as well as the place where food was prepared and cooked. Ancient beams in a low ceiling were supported by four wooden posts.

Against the wall facing the door stood a large Welsh dresser whose three lower shelves were extensively decorated with blue and white willow-pattern china. On the rim of the top shelf hung a row of eight pewter mugs. Below them stood a line of souvenir china jugs depicting various giants of the Welsh Baptist Pulpit. The whole edifice had a conspicuous symmetry; it seemed to me that nothing had been moved from it since my last visit. The massive oak beam which spanned the large open fireplace had, according to my uncle, been taken centuries ago from a galleon wrecked in the Bristol Channel. Its scorch marks made me think of pirates, cutlasses, boarding parties, smugglers, and barrels of rum. Not for the first time the fantasy of an old-time sailor's life filled my head.

When we used to visit Caerwen with my mother, Gareth and I would invariably have to sit and listen to Bopa Mari's everlasting tales of woe. We would count the jugs on the dresser, stare at the sleeping spaniels and the rugs on the floor, and listen to the interminable ticking of the grandfather clock in the corner. Sometimes Uncle Gwilym would mercifully rescue us from the stultifying boredom with an invitation to see new-born lambs and calves; or just to sit down for a chat about things historical.

Walter and I entered the room to find that Bopa Mari wasn't there, but on the huge table were several dishes covered with white cloths, which we removed to reveal an assortment of mouth-watering food.

'I take back what I said about yewer aunty,' said my friend, attacking an egg sandwich. 'She's got a kind side to 'er, after all.'

'No,' I said, 'it's my uncle who did this. He always does.'

'Bloody 'ell!' said Walter, wiping the back of his hand across his chin before reaching for a succulent piece of roast chicken. 'Well, fancy that – I wish *I* 'ad an uncle like 'im!'

A bowl of cold new potatoes with mint sauce was quickly emptied. Tomatoes, boiled beetroot, and crisp sticks of celery were duly made to disappear, as was a large wedge of Welsh cheese along with its rind. By the time we'd seen off cold rhubarb pie with cream and sampled some of Uncle Gwilym's home-made nettle beer we wondered if we were still able to walk.

We trudged slowly back towards the village. By the time we reached the stile at the bottom of *Cae Twm Tincer* we were bound to stop for a rest. The five hundred yards we'd travelled had felt more like five hundred miles. We still felt extremely bloated and I said to Walter that I felt I might burst at any moment.

'Me, too,' he said. 'But if that 'appens, there won't be much left of us by mornin' – those bloody Llwynybrain rooks will see to that. I think I can 'ear 'em now. Come on, let's keep goin'.'

A short cut across Penygarn field brought us to the rear of Pegler's shop where Mr Smitherham was wheeling sacks of maize from the back of a lorry.

Seeing us, he said, 'Hey, whadda're you'm pair a-doin' of 'ere, then?'

'What do yew mean?' said Walter. ''Aven't we got a right to be by 'ere, then?'

'It bain't that,' said Smitherham. 'It's why bain't you up them trees with them others, 'sno? Don' 'appen to approve of un mysel, but today be the day, baint it?'

'Jesus!' cried Walter. 'Let's go, Geraint! We'll miss the bloody *Crossing*!'

'Thank you, Mr Smitherham,' I said as we rushed away.

Chapter Nine

The Crossing! How could we have forgotten it!

'No wonder we couldn't see no bugger!' panted Walter as we ran. '*They* 'adn't forgotten about it, 'ad they?'

We arrived at the headland of *Cae'r Cwtyn*, The Plover's Field, to find that almost the whole of Pengarth youth were there for our greatest annual event. We'd heard that about thirty boys between the ages of ten and fourteen were taking part.

The event was known as 'tree climbing with a difference'. Competitors first had to scale the big beech at the bottom of *Cae Bronllwyn* by means of a rope-ladder. Between that and the end of the course was a line of eighteen trees of various types and sizes that they had to traverse without touching the ground. Wil Mathews had told me that my grandfather was the best of his generation, informing me with a perfectly straight face that in those days the trees had been further apart.

Apparently the earlier rounds for the younger boys had passed off uneventfully. I wasn't sorry to have missed them for my incurable dread of heights had always precluded me from competing.

But the heroes were now getting ready to start, their efforts to be measured against the clock. I felt both proud and apprehensive to see Gareth limbering up near the base of the first tree. The evacuees, too, had fielded a few useful climbers, including Ronnie and somewhat improbably the plump Terenzis. The Marks brothers, who by now had been comfortably installed with the kindly Mrs Emmy Howells, were also taking part. They weren't exactly rookies either, for they had already demonstrated an impressive skill at shinning up tele-graph poles. As practice on the actual trees was forbidden, many of the competitors were first-timers.

'If I was a bookie I'd be takin' bets from yew lot,' said Walter to a nearby group.

'All right, you clever sod,' said Idwal Thomas. 'Who's the bloody favourite, then?'

'Gareth Llewellyn, of course, yew idiot,' said Walter. 'This 'un's big brother. He won it last year, an' 'e'll probably win it this time, too. As if yew didn't bloody know.'

This made Idwal angry and he went for Walter, whose neat sidestep caused his assailant to lunge into a patch of bramble which effectively scratched away any residual enthusiasm for physical violence. Straightening up he said, 'All right, Oppy, you sod. I don't want to 'it a bloody cripple, do I? But you just bloody watch it, innit. *Just bloody watch it*!' And he walked off.

Walter smiled at me. *'Duw*, mun! I wish I 'ad his wonderful way with words!'

The litle rumpus had brought over the referee Gwyn Jones, the vicar's son. 'Look lads,' he said. 'Let's have a bit of respect, shall we? This is serious stuff. I mean, *lives* are being risked, aren't they?'

My God, yes! I thought. And that includes Gareth's. I'd forgotten just how dangerous The Crossing was. Suddenly I had to be sick. I went behind a tree and took perhaps a full minute to relieve myself of the remains of what I had so fool-ishly stuffed myself with at Caerwen. I felt better immediately and also considerably less worried about Gareth.

'Do yew always go white when yew 'ave a leak?' said Walter, as I rejoined him. 'Yew look as if yew've seen a bloody ghost.'

'I've just been sick,' I said. 'I ate too much at Caerwen.'

'Yew didn't eat more than I did,' said Walter. 'And I feel OK.'

'That's because you've got hollow legs,' I said.

'Let's go and watch by Number Eight,' said Walter. 'They'll 'ave no trouble gettin' as far as that. From there on, though, it'll be brown trousers stuff.'

We heard about the early failures. Groucho Marks had gone first and had fallen at the third tree. Harpo went next and did one better than his brother, crashing down from the field maple.

Each of the Terenzis had made it to Number Eight, the Welsh oak, and Walter was right: getting from its branches to those of the next, a rather spindly willow, would always be a challenge. I was to learn later that the only way to do it was to lie along one of the slender branches of the oak and allow one's weight to bring it down slowly into the middle of the willow; rather like the way another trunk would gently lower Sabu to the ground in the film 'Elephant Boy'. Both Terenzis had made the mistake of going too far out on the oak branch, hitting the ground hard enough to generate a torrent of Italian curses.

Walter put his arm around my shoulder and said, 'Don't worry, Ger. Yewer brother can do this blindfold with one arm tied behind his bloody back!'

Yes, of course he can, I thought. He's Gareth. He knows Kipling's 'If' off by heart and he knows how to make girls go weak-kneed.

I thought of Annabel and wondered if she was around. After all, her brother was taking part and was already standing at the foot of the first tree.

The late afternoon sunlight was reflected in the polished copper and brass of the referee's hunting horn.

'Next competitor . . . Ronnie Webb!' shouted Gwyn, and blew a loud *Pheeoop! Pheeoop!* that came echoing back from the houses two fields away.

While I was imagining the hounds at the Garth kennels suddenly being thrown into a frenzy by the unseasonal sound and all the local foxes diving for cover, Ronnie Webb was going up the beech like a monkey.

Walter and I followed Ronnie as he went from tree to tree, finally to complete the course in thirty-two minutes. I couldn't help feeling sorry that Annabel hadn't been there to witness her brother's very creditable performance.

A few others had also finished the course, but so far none had achieved a time to compare with Ronnie's.

Finally it was the turn of the last competitor – Gareth. According to the rules he had won this privilege by winning the previous year's event. I found some of my previous anxiety returning, but I needn't have worried. My brother scrambled and swung his way through the first seven trees like a latter-day Tarzan; then he reached Number Eight . . .

'This is where 'e'll come unstuck,' said Huw Williams, a local Jeremiah.

'Why don't yew just piss off, yew miserable bugger,' said Walter.

My God, I said to myself. I hope this doesn't start a fight. That'll be the last thing we'll need.

'It's quite simple really,' said Gwyn Jones, 'it's all to do with the laws of mechanics. Gareth will know what to do.' He then waffled on about moments of force and fulcra, whatever *they* were.

'What the 'ell is 'e rantin' about? Is 'e talkin' English, or what?' said Walter to me.

'Well, I can tell you it's not Welsh,' I said, hoping he wouldn't pursue the matter, as I was equally baffled.

'I'll *tell* you what it is,' said Gwyn. 'It's *leverage*. Simple as that. It's all a matter of leverage.'

'Same as a bloody see-saw, then,' said Walter.

'Exactly,' said the vicar's son. '*Just* like a bloody see-saw. You're not just a pretty face, are you, Walter?'

In the event, Gareth went from the oak to the willow with precision. He then dealt expertly with two elms, a crab apple, three further stunted oaks and two silver birches, before coming to a sudden halt at the penultimate – a massive elm. Looking somewhat bewildered, he called down to the referee.

'Gwyn!' he shouted. 'Someone's sawn through a branch!'

The referee was lifted onto the shoulders of a sturdy youth for a detailed examination of the stump that was about ten feet up from the base of the beech. He came down to face the crowd and announced solemnly that the saw-marks were fresh. 'This was obviously done within the last half hour.'

'But who would do such an awful thing?' said Bethan Thomas, who adored my brother.

'I bet yew a pound to a pinch of polecat poop, it's Dilwyn,' said Walter. 'I'll get that devil one day if it's the last bloody thing I do!'

'Well, that's it,' said Gwyn to Gareth. 'Come down, then. The event is over.' Everyone groaned.

'Hang on a minute!' cried Gareth, 'I think I can see another branch. I'm going to have a go, anyway. Nothing ventured, nothing gained!'

'Christ,' said Walter, 'yewer brother's talking like Gwyn Jones. It must be bloody catchin'.'

'Well, they go to the same school,' I said, wishing for once that Walter would shut up. I was sure Gareth was about to do something pretty dangerous despite the referee's pleading.

'Far too dangerous!' cried Gwyn. 'That branch is at least fifteen feet from the ground and twelve feet away from you. Not on, Gareth! Don't be stupid. Come down.'

Gareth made no reply and began to climb to a new position. We had no choice but to resign ourselves to the inevitable. Walter put his hand on my shoulder and said: 'Don't yew worry, 'e'll do it; yew'll see!'

Next thing, Gareth was swinging through the air, finally to wrap his arms around a branch of the last tree. Gwyn Jones clicked his stopwatch and announced amid loud applause that my brother had come home in twenty-nine minutes and three seconds – possibly a record.

There was a loud crack as the branch holding Gareth snapped, sending him plummeting to the ground. With my heart in my mouth I ran up to him and said, 'Are you all right?'

'I think so,' he said. He was obviously being brave but I could tell from his expression that he must have been in a lot of pain.

'Can you walk?' I said.

'I don't know,' he said, still wincing. 'I can try.'

Walter and I helped him to his feet, but after a few steps his leg buckled and he collapsed.

'He must have a doctor!' cried Bethan Thomas. 'I think he might've broken his leg!'

Oh God, no! I thought.

I looked around for Walter but he was nowhere to be seen. Angrily I wondered why he had chosen to disappear at this of all times.

However, Gwyn Jones and Ronnie had readily agreed to help to get Gareth home.

Accompanied by a small crowd they slowly moved away. It took us all of twenty minutes to get out of the field but on reaching the road we were delighted and astonished to see Dr Glennie standing by her car parked near the gate.

'In here, if you'd be so good,' said the doctor, holding open one of the rear doors of the Austin. Gwyn Jones helped Gareth onto the back seat and was allowed to accompany him to the surgery. Ronnie and I gave them a wave as they left.

'He'll be all right now, Geraint, won't he?' said a much relieved Bethan Thomas. 'Dr Glennie'll put him right.'

'Of course she will,' I said. 'I'm sure of it.'

That belied my true feelings, for I was still quite worried.

I didn't hurry home because I wasn't expected for at least another hour; in any case I wanted to think.

Ambling around he headlands of the Penllwyn top fields, well away from the village, I reflected on a most unusual day. We'd saved a little pig's life, shod a Welsh prince, feasted grandly, and seen a brother injured. But most remarkable was the annoying and inexplicable disappearance of Walter.

My mother came into the big room carrying a plate of Spam, mashed potatoes, and peas, and asked the question that I'd been dreading:

'Where's Gareth?' And then, 'He should be back from the surgery by now.' Naturally I was very relieved, but wondered how she could have known what had happened.

She looked rather worried. 'Mr Smitherham's been here,' she said. 'On his way home from Pegler's he called to tell me that Gareth had fallen from a tree. He needed some bandaging, so Doctor Glennie had taken him with her to do a proper job. But it wasn't serious because the doctor told Mr Smitherham that nothing is broken and that he'll soon be all right again.'

I got up from the table and gave her a hug.

Shortly afterwards Gareth came home with a bandaged leg and a broad smile.

'Back from the dead!' he said, giving me a friendly clip on the ear. 'Indestructible, that's me.'

Later in bed I said, 'It's been a strange day, Gar, hasn't it?'

'Oh? In what way?'

'Well, it's been very eventful for one thing. But I think the strangest thing of all was Walter disappearing like he did.' And I explained to Gareth what had happened.

'Well, I can tell you this,' said Gareth. 'It was Walter who ran to the Post Office to ask them to telephone the doctor. That's why she got there so quickly.'

Chapter Ten

There were periods when we were lulled into putting the war to the back of our minds. Our rural life was mostly still bathed in tranquility and some local matters remained paramount. This was apparent to me when I eavesdropped on a conversation between the village bobby and Sam 'Tidy' Thomas, the roadsweeper. The day-long sounds of Sam's hard bass broom scouring the roadside and of his *cryman* (sickle) shaving any grasses that had dared to overgrow on the banks were as familiar to me as birdsong. But now, in a rare moment of inactivity, he stood on the crossroads near the village police station showing the contents of his little trolley to King the Copper. The words I heard left me in no doubt that even if the Axis threw its mightiest divisions at us, Sam and those like him would get their priorities right.

'Another dead hedgehog, Mr King,' said Sam. 'That's the second one this week.'

We were reminded, however, that there was indeed 'a war on' long before the end of the school holidays. The sounds of aircraft became more frequent and the searchlight and artillery battery unit on the Garth seemed to be on almost constant alert. During raids over Cardiff and the nearby Treforest Trading Estate we inevitably caught some of the fall-out and soon became remarkably efficient in dealing with it.

Walter and I had enjoyed watching the lessons in stirrup-pump operation. On one occasion Eaglebeak got drenched as the result of an accidentally 'wandering nozzle'. Well, the stirrup-pump student *claimed* it was accidental. Whatever it was it was much enjoyed by all who witnessed it. Walter and I did a little dance. Eaglebeak, of course, was considerably less amused.

Shortly after eleven o'clock one night in early September local fire-fighting skills were put to the real test. The warning wail of the siren had scarcely died away before the first incendiaries arrived. Dozens fell on and around the village and later it seemed almost miraculous that Shoni 'One Eye' Jenkins's bungalow was the only dwelling to suffer any real damage. It was just down the lane from our house and Gareth and I, who were forbidden to go outside, watched fascinated from our bedroom window as the stirrup-pump brigade suppported by a chain of water-bearers dealt with the blaze in the old boy's kitchen.

It took about twenty minutes before the last flame was extinguished. Shoni in the meantime had been given shelter and sustenance in our house, Dad having been among the first to arrive on the scene. My father said later that Shoni, an ex-collier whò had also survived the carnage of Passchendaele in 1917, had surprised my mother during his graphic description of what he would like to do to those Germans responsible for his present distress. Dad said that he had later been quite embarrassed while endeavouring to explain the meaning of one or two words and expressions that she'd never heard before . . .

On another occasion an unmistakeable whine heralded the advent of something more immediately alarming than a few incendiaries. The huge bomb fell a quarter of a mile away in a field of Pantygored farm. An enormous explosion shook the whole village, rattling windows and even dislodging a slate or two. Fortunately there was no human injury or trauma; unless, of course, one considers the case of Sam Tidy. The roadman's description of his bitter ordeal as he sat in the lavatory during and after that hellish bang was utterly hilarious; and quite unprintable.

When daylight came crowds made their way to Pantygored to see the crater and the consensus was that the bomb had been jettisoned by a fugitive aircraft.

The harmlessness of that event was in sharp contrast to what happened a week later to a house in Pantygored Road. A stray incendiary bomb had lodged in a corner of the roof and before the NFS arrived the whole house was hopelessly ablaze. It would be the only dwelling in the parish destroyed by enemy action.

Before eight o'clock in the morning Walter and I were among a crowd of sightseers. Men were already clearing debris despite the fact that quite a lot of it was still smouldering. We had promised to be back at my house by nine as my mother was taking Walter and me to Cardiff. On the way home we found a couple of green, seven-inch-long incendiary bomb tail-fins. Walter didn't want one, so my own collection of tail-fins would now number thirteen.

My mother had said that no German bombers were going to stop her going into Cardiff. She'd been looking forward to it for weeks, and although she didn't say so, it would be her first trip into town since my father's promotion. Now she would have more money to spend.

'Just enough time for a wash before we go,' said Mam, taking the big iron kettle from the fire and pouring the water into the enamelled bowl normally used for quick swills. Walter and I both stripped to the waist and scrubbed ourselves in the same water, the carbolic soap drawing tears from our eyes and getting up our noses.

When we'd finished, Mam said, 'Well done. You are both shining now. *Fel tlysa.* Like jewels.'

Handing us a big towel she sent us to the communal tap-house for the rinse. 'Hurry up now or we'll miss the bus,' she said. 'Did you know that a Gary Cooper film is showing at the Olympia?'

That sent us to the tap-house like a pair of greyhounds. We got there to find our way to the tap blocked by Gwilym Morgan and Penry Davies who were discussing the progress of the war.

'Excuse me, Mr Morgan,' I said. 'We are in a bit of a hurry. We've got a bus to catch and we must have a rinse quickly!'

'Certainly sir,' said Mr Morgan, with a mock salute as he stepped aside.

We got off the bus at Park Place. Before making for Queen Street, which not only had the best shops but also the best cinemas, we paused as we always did to admire some of the finest civic buildings in Europe: the City Hall, the Law Courts, and the National Museum of Wales. The early autumn sunshine enhanced the beauty of the splendid white buildings. Neither the abundant sandbags nor the nearby concrete air-raid shelters could diminish the magnificence of Cathays Park.

Our route to the town centre took us alongside the canal feeder and the short cut down the lane near the gaunt ruin of the old Friary. Our first call in Queen Street should have been the Carlton Restaurant, or at least that part of it which had previously been a popular doughnut shop and café, but lately had only been offering unappealing wartime buns. We would have sat down at a table while my mother ordered tea for herself, a milkshake each for Walter and me, and some toasted teacakes.

However, before we were within a hundred yards of the Carlton we knew something was wrong. A pungent smell hung in the air and as we drew near we saw people crowding around a barrier attended by special policemen. By the time we reached

Queen Street we could see that our beloved Carlton had been reduced to a smouldering ruin.

'Oh dear, oh dear,' said Mam, visibly moved. '*What* a terrible shame!'

Being deprived of eagerly awaited refreshment was bad enough, but very soon there would be more bad news. Forty yards down Queen Street we found one of our favourite places of entertainment the Empire Cinema cordoned off, too; and, of course, closed!

Incendiaries had gutted several shops and a high-explosive bomb had destroyed Peacock's store, now little more than a heap of rubble. Workmen were attending to a burst water main nearby, but couldn't prevent a side road looking like the Glamorganshire Canal. Water was starting to creep into the shops and offices of Charles Street and many people in doorways were busy with their brushes. Others were stealing sandbags from the front of The Midland Bank and hastily making new barriers against the flood.

A huge fire engine blocked the front entrance to Marks and Spencer's, so we followed my mother through a side door where Walter and I paused before a large notice that declared:

> *'The management wish to thank the night staff and wardens for their alertness and courage in saving your favourite store from serious damage during last night's air-aid.'*

Feeling that Walter would have difficulty with this, I read it to him.

'What's alertness mean, Ger?' he said.

'*Duw,*' I said, with my tongue in my cheek. 'That's a *hard* one Walt!'

'What d'yew mean?' said Walter. 'Don't yew know?'

'Course I do.'

114

'Well, what is it, then?'

'Well,' I said, already feeling that I was pushing my luck. 'It means dedication.'

'Well, it don't, see! It means bein' watchful and ready to act. That's what it means. *That's* why they call an air-raid warnin' the "alert", innit? *Yew* should know that, clever dick! Yewer Welsh may be OK, but yewer English isn't very good, is it?'

My joke had rebounded and there was nothing I could do about it.

My mother, who had gone ahead of us, returned to ask why we were dawdling.

By the time we left the store I was the proud owner of new short trousers, stockings, and shoes; likewise Walter, for my mother was the soul of kindness.

Next stop was Woolworth's, a shop that must have been designed in paradise. We snaked around the counters, one of which contained an irresistible mass of hot, salted, roasted peanuts – with a sublime flavour like no other! We stopped here and there while Mam bought such essentials as needles, cotton, buttons, a writing pad, envelopes, a new tin-opener, a stick of shaving soap, and a booklet on a hundred-and-one things to make from dried egg.

On our way to the cafeteria we passed a certain section that I decided I would visit at the earliest opportunity.

I loved the stools at the cafeteria bar because they had round upholstered seats that swivelled. I also loved the food. When in town we would sometimes eat at the British Restaurant in St Mary Street, one of a nationwide network set up by the Government to provide simple wholesome food. However, I always found a Woolworth's meal more enjoyable. The juicy meat pies were marvellous: soft, flaky crust, succulent lumps of beef, and tasty gravy; they contained just enough salt to titillate the taste buds into wanting more. The gods on Olympus would certainly have approved of Woolworth's meat pies.

After our meal my mother ordered a pot of tea, whereupon I excused myself to go to the toilet. I was pleased Walter didn't join me because I wanted to be alone at that counter which had previously caught my interest.

I stood in front of an array of scent-bottles, some of which had spray- heads and little rubber bulbs for squeezing. Many had exotic names and tiny ribbon-bows around their necks. Such a wide choice was overwhelming and I wondered what they all smelt like: *Ashes of Roses; Evening in Paris; Apple Blossom* . . . the one called *Perfumes from the Palms* made me think of sweaty hands.

Most of the bottles I fancied were priced at three shillings, sixpence more than the last half-crown Uncle Gwilym had given me for helping at the farm. Fearful that my mother would come looking for me, I began to feel a little panicky; and it must have showed because a plump lady of about seventeen came over to ask if she could help me.

I told her I wanted a nice bottle of scent for a special young girl but had only half-a-crown.

'Oh, I see,' she said with a smile and a strong Cardiff accent. 'I think we can do something about that.'

She removed the stopper from a small bottle and asked me to sniff the contents.

'That's nice,' I said. 'What's it called?'

'It's jasmine,' she replied. 'Lovely, isn't it?'

'Yes, it's beautiful. How much is it?'

'Believe it or not,' she said. 'It's two-and-six. But to you, only half-a-crown.'

'You were a long time,' said Mam as she and Walter slipped off the barstools and turned for the exit. 'Never mind, we've still got enough time to get to the Olympia before the big picture starts.'

Good, I thought. Missing the start of a Gary Cooper film was unimaginable.

'Sergeant York' wasn't a cowboy film, but a First World War epic in which the exploits of a crack-shot soldier were greatly exaggerated, claiming that he wiped out single-handedly numerous machine-gun posts and captured 132 prisoners! Gary Cooper, of course, was born to play the part of Alvin York.

We enjoyed the film immensely; likewise the supporting feature, a Laurel and Hardy classic. The intervening newsreel showed the awesome dangers faced by convoys in the Atlantic and elsewhere. The coverage of the relentless blitz on London certainly put our local air-raids into perspective.

Coming out of a cinema and back into the real world was always disorientating and it usually took a minute or two to readjust.

With time to spare before the bus was due to leave we joined a small crowd that had gathered on the canal bridge at Kingsway. They were throwing coins into the water below, where small boys in swimming trunks were diving in from the towpath to retrieve them. My mother handed a sixpenny piece to each of us.

'That's a fortune,' said Walter, 'I'd dive in myself for that!'

My mother smiled. 'Go on, throw it, Walter,' she said. 'Those boys need the money more than you do.'

Walter and I threw our coins and immediately two black lads of about our age disappeared into the canal, emerging a few seconds later each with with a coin between his teeth.

'*Ardderchog!*' shouted Mam.

'That means Excellent!' I called down to them.

Back in our village Walter thanked my mother sincerely before he left us, carrying the brown paper bag that contained his new clothes.

'I hope his mother won't mind,' said Mam in Welsh after he'd gone. 'But it must be hard for them with all those children.'

My father and Gareth had prepared a home-grown meal for us. Potatoes fresh from the soil, tender runner beans, and sweet crimson beetroot, were very welcome, but there was an extra treat.

'Chicken!' gasped my mother. 'We've got *chicken*!'

'Yes,' said Dad. 'When I went round to see Jemima Jenkins this morning she wiped her knife on her apron and went straight out to the chicken run.'

'But why today?' asked my mother as she prepared a bowl of hot water and soap for us to wash our hands.

'Because we are celebrating something, that's why.'

'Celebrating? Something to do with your new job?'

'No.'

'The war?'

'No.'

Gareth was wearing a big smile as we took our places at the table. He obviously knew something. My mother appealed once more for an explanation.

'I'll give you a clue,' said Dad. It was beginning to sound like one of those guessing games on the wireless.

My father contemplated a forkful of chicken before continuing. 'Dan Powell has been here,' he said.

'*Councillor* Powell?' said my mother. 'What could he be wanting?'

'He wanted to break the good news to us.'

'No more teasing, Trefor. Just tell us, will you' said my mother, playfully trying to slap him.

Dad ducked and dodged and decided to end the suspense.

'We've been granted a council house,' he said, trying to sound casual. This was tremendous news! I knew that my parents had long been trying for a new house, but we wondered if the dream would ever come true.

Mam got up slowly as Dad continued to recall Councillor Powell's visit. She walked around the room and for a few moments was speechless, until, shedding tears of joy, she turned and hugged us one by one. *'Diolch i'r Arglwydd,'* she said, repeatedly. 'Thank the Lord.'

We sat talking about the ways in which our quality of life would improve in a semi-detached house that had a side entrance, a separate kitchen, a bathroom, and water that came out of taps. And the lavatory: no longer a wooden bench with a round hole in it and a bucket below; moreover, it wouldn't be forty yards from the house and smelling of Jeyes Fluid.

Things were getting easier all round for our family. The fact that Dad could now return from the quarry in clean clothes meant less work for my mother. On returning to school, Gareth, now fifteen, would be taking his Central Welsh Board examinations early as he was well advanced for his age. As for me, I would be getting my second chance at the Scholarship.

Our father had all but given up the drink and was continuing with his studies as well as giving time to the amateur dramatic society that had recently started in Pengarth. Now the prospect of moving to a better house turned a happy home into an ecstatic one.

Oddly enough, I knew I would miss many of the features of our old house. The sashcord window in our bedroom would certainly be one. The pantry and the stone slab. The big fireplace with its blackleaded grate and iron kettle would be things of the past in our fully electrified home. I was wondering if Gareth over in the other bed had the same sentimental thoughts; I noticed he was immersed in a recently acquired copy of *Vanity Fair*.

Suddenly he looked up. 'Just think, Ger,' he said, 'no more carrying water-jacks.'

'Too true!' I said.

Chapter Eleven

The first chilly autumn breezes held back until the day we returned to school for the new term in mid-September. With the wind came the kind of rain that finds its way under collars and into boots. The playground was strewn with rain-soaked leaves from the sycamores and chestnuts that hung over the wall. Ahead of us would be those dank, dreary, endless school-days, seemingly designed as penance for the sin of being young rather than for learning in an atmosphere of joy.

There was one teacher, though, who could lighten the darkest days. I liked Miss Mary Thomas very much and knowing that I would now be joining her class helped greatly to mollify my dread of the return to school. She had already been our Art and Music teacher and her entertaining approach to the work would ensure my rapt attention.

In April she ordered from *The Children's Newspaper* a con-signment of silkworm eggs for us to oversee their hatching and growing to maturity. The metamorphosis from caterpillar to moth via the chrysalis and cocoon stages would end with the slow production of silk. The excitement caused by this prospect was almost unbearable.

Each pupil had a matchbox containing about a dozen eggs the size of pinheads. After hatching, in the absence of mulberry leaves, the worms were fed on lettuce, and over a few weeks the creatures grew from hair-like objects into inch-long caterpillars as thick as bootlaces. However, we arrived at school one morning to find that all our little charges had died overnight; each one had expired and fallen off the leaf that had been both its bed and its breakfast. As the caterpillars had seemed healthy enough the previous afternoon no one could explain the tragic event. Someone suggested unconvincingly that the creatures had been homesick for China and had died of broken hearts.

'Nah, maybe it was the lettuce,' offered Peter Lawton. 'After all, it's not their proper food. Fancy 'avin' to eat bloody lettuce all day.'

'OK if you're a rabbit,' said Mike Terenzi. 'We had rabbits and that's all they ever bloody ate. They grew as big as dogs.'

'Rubbish,' said Walter, limping towards us. 'Do yew think they all decided to bugger off at the same time to that great bloody mulberry bush in the sky? Like a mass soddin' suicide or somethin'? Nah, 'smore likely to be Dilwyn who did it!' And with a sideways look at me he added, 'That's another one we owe 'im!'

I felt it unlikely that the rascal had crept into the school at night and poisoned the worms. Anyway, Miss Thomas with typical thoughtfulness ordered another batch of eggs.

Most of these also reached the bootlace stage before dying. This time Dilwyn was exonerated, for the creatures often gave up the will to live before our very eyes. The few dozen that survived were being fed on mulberry leaves recently obtained from the gardens of Tŷ Mawr. Although it was now obvious that the lettuce had been responsible for the caterpillars' demise, no one felt remorse for having blamed Dilwyn. His infamy would easily stand the test of an occasional mistaken accusation.

The surviving caterpillars had been in glowing health when Miss Thomas took them home for care during the summer holidays. Yet again we were to hear of a catastrophe involving the creatures and, much more seriously, Miss Thomas herself. At Assembly Eaglebeak called for attention with three smacks of his cane on a table.

'I am afraid I have some sad news for you,' said the headmaster. 'Miss Thomas will not be here today. The Cardiff suburb of Whitchurch where she has lived for years suffered greatly during last night's bombing.' He pursed his lips and slapped his free hand with the cane. It occurred to me that if Rockfist or Gary had needed an able lieutenant on a mission to assassinate Hitler, Eaglebeak would have been the man.

'These murderous heathens have once again shown they have no regard for innocent civilians in this conflict!'

'My God,' I thought, 'what could have happened to Miss Thomas? Surely she can't be *dead*? Why doesn't he get on with it and tell us the truth?' My sense of dread was obviously shared, for all around me there were sighs and the lowering of heads.

'You will be pleased to hear,' he said, slowly taking out his pocket-watch, more for dramatic effect than to check the time, 'that Miss Mary Thomas is safe and uninjured.' A huge sigh resounded about the school hall.

'I have here,' he said, holding a sheet of paper high at arms length, 'a message for you from your teacher.'

Dear children,

I am afraid I cannot be with you for a short while because enemy bombers paid a visit to our neighbourhood last night and did some nasty things. It was rather naughty of them to turn my home into a heap of rubble, especially as it had only recently been decorated. War is a terrible thing which brings out the worst but also the best in people. Some day I shall tell you of the courage shown by my neighbours amidst the heat, the noise, and the pain of that nightmarish experience. Also of the brightness and the smiles I see all around me this morning from people who have lost nearly everything but who are determined to get on with their lives. I have some good news for you. One of the silk-

worms was found unharmed in its box this morning. It is fat and bonny and, I dare say, looking forward as much as I am to our return to school. Be good and do well in your lessons. I will be back as soon as I can! My love and best wishes to you all.

M. Thomas

Mr Lewis took our class in the absence of Miss Thomas and, despite his strictness, was a lot more acceptable than our 'Mrs Brownbum', who had continued her habit of sending kids to Eaglebeak for punishment at the slightest excuse. Walter had more stripes on him than a zebra.

After about two weeks Miss Thomas came back, and for once Eaglebeak turned a blind eye to the breakdown in decorum which occurred when she was mobbed by a swarm of the younger children, each of whom she hugged in turn. There was also the triumphant homecoming of the sole surviving silkworm to celebrate. Lying in its display box at the front of class it looked like a crumpled dried-up little sausage and appeared to be quite dead. Our teacher assured us that it was in fact very much alive and in the chrysalis stage, later to be cocooned in silk.

Miss Thomas explained that two brave neighbours had left their shelter and entered the blazing house to rescue, among other things, the tin box which had been home to the caterpillars during the August break. By morning the box had cooled and the survivor was found munching mulberry unconcernedly.

'I think we should give it a name, don't you?' said Miss Thomas, getting out of her desk and moving towards the blackboard. 'Let's have some suggestions, then.' She looked around the classroom with chalk in hand.

'Please, Miss, is it a he or a she?' I felt a thrill as I heard the girl's voice. It was Annabel, standing prettily in the front row with an arm raised. As she stood there, flicking a stray strand of hair over her shoulder, my infatuation reasserted itself.

'That's a good question, Annabel,' said Miss Thomas. 'Neither, actually. Neither a he nor a she as we understand it. So you can call it whatever you like.'

'What about "Helen" then? May we call it "Helen"?' asked Annabel, dropping her arm and and sitting down all in one beautiful movement.

Miss Thomas duly wrote 'Helen' on the board and asked if there were any more suggestions. I was thinking that the only other Helen I knew of was a pig, when my best friend stood up.

'"Lazarus",' said Walter, causing every head to turn. 'Yeah, "Lazarus" . . . like the bloke who came back from the dead, see.'

Uproar. Even Miss Thomas laughed loudly and added her own little joke by thanking Walter for pointing out that Lazarus came from the Dead Sea.

'Very good, Walter, but I don't think we should call it "Lazarus",' said the teacher kindly. 'Let's have some more names, then.'

Hands went up like spears. 'Miss, Miss, Miss.' In minutes the blackboard was full.

Alexander . . . Owain . . . Gary . . . George . . . Winston . . .

'That's interesting,' said Miss Thomas, 'They are all men's names except one. Well, I never! I like "Helen" myself and that's what it'll be. Anyone else like "Helen"? If so, raise your hand.'

I felt my arm rising. I couldn't stop it. If the class thought I was being ingratiating, the girl who turned around and smiled at me knew otherwise.

Over a week or so Helen became hidden under a tuft of silk about the size of a bantam's egg. Its colour was somewhere between pink and gold, looking not unlike candyfloss. Under a magnifying glass we could see that it was in fact a continuous silken thread wound with precision around whatever was left of

Helen inside. Each pupil was allowed to touch the silk to feel its softness.

Then came the great day. We were each asked to write our names on pieces of paper to find a boy and a girl who would have the honour of unravelling the thread, and someone was sent to fetch Eaglebeak to make the draw. Walter often said that Eaglebeak was in love with Miss Thomas and that the only time he ever smiled was when she was near him. When the headmaster entered the classroom he was smirking. Walter turned around in his desk and gave me a 'thumbs up' sign.

It was inevitable that Eaglebeak would have something to say before making the draw and he took the opportunity to say how lucky we all were to have such a fine person as Miss Thomas to be our teacher. The woman appeared to be somewhat embarrassed. His speech over, the headmaster put to the class a question that caused several hands to be instantly raised.

'Who knows the Welsh word for silk?' he asked and without drawing breath said, 'No, no, no, not you Welsh-speakers! Does anyone who can't speak Welsh know what our word for silk is?'

'I know what it is in Italian,' said Michael Terenzi. I thought the evacueee might as well have signed his own death warrant, but presumably the presence of Miss Thomas calmed the headmaster, whose reaction was mild to say the least. He just pointed his cane at the boy and said:

'Didn't you wash your ears this morning? I said Welsh, not Italian!'

No other hand was raised so he turned the question over to the Welsh speakers who shouted in perfect unison, *'Sidan*, sir!' pronouncing the word the East Glamorgan way as *sheetan.*

'Now, then,' said Eaglebeak, with almost a hint of kindness in his voice, 'we can hear what it is in Italian.' Together the Terenzi twins stood up and said: *'Seta*, sir, *la seta.'*

'Quite right, quite right,' said Eaglebeak, nodding. I felt sure he hadn't known the answer himself but it was unlikely that he would have displayed his ignorance in front of the woman he apparently loved so much!

Eaglebeak drew two pieces of paper from the box and passed them to Miss Thomas who unfolded them and read out the names.

'The first is Annabel, Annabel Webb,' said the teacher. 'And may I say how pleased I am that the girl who chose the creature's name will now help with the unravelling of the silk.' Naturally *I* was pleased, too!

'And the second name is Walter Hopkins.'

I felt more than a tinge of envy and briefly thought my loyalty to my best friend was going to be tested. However, I quickly recovered my good sense and began to feel pleased for him. Had I not done so, in a moment I would have been even more disconcerted.

'Please, Miss Thomas,' said Walter, as he rose from his desk. 'Please, Miss, I think Geraint should take my place, cos it was 'e 'oo agreed with the name isn't it?'

'Well, I'm sure I don't mind' said the teacher with a shrug. 'Anyone else mind?'

As there was no response I found myself standing at the front of class with Annabel beside me. There was another 'thumbs' up sign from Walter. One day that boy will surely be something important, I thought. Perhaps Prime Minister.

Eaglebeak stood there for a few moments shaking his head, and after looking at his watch he nodded to the teacher and left the room.

'Well, it really is time we were getting on with this,' said Miss Thomas. 'I'm sure Helen is anxious to get unwrapped.'

Susie Gainsborough, who had been sent to the kitchen, returned with a basin of hot water which she placed on a table positioned out front for all to have a good view. There was a gasp from the class as Miss Thomas plunged the silken-coated Helen into the water.

It all seemed wonderful to me. Miraculous and beautiful.

Annabel and I sat on chairs facing each other. I was to hold the cocoon by means of a pin inserted in each end and Annabel was to wind the thread around a piece of card on which Miss Thomas had carefully written the name of our school and the date. After removing the cocoon from the hot water Miss Thomas, using the magnifier, located the leading end of the silk strand with a pair of tweezers. She carefully loosened the thread and wound a short length around the card before handing over to Annabel. I was required to revolve the cocoon slowly in order to ease the release of the silk as Annabel wound it on, and from time to time it had to be re-immersed in the hot water to help loosen the thread. Miss Thomas instructed Annabel to nod each time she felt ready to make a winding so that I would revolve the cocoon simultaneously to lessen the risk of snapping the thread. Soon we fell into a rhythm and it was so good to be close to the most beautiful girl in the world who, now and again, smiled at me!

No words passed between us and only once did I squander a moment of the precious time with a quick glance at Walter from whom I got another 'thumbs up'.

When the last strand was unwound I felt some misgiving when I saw all that was left of the wretched Helen lying there, dry and shrivelled. I had seen bigger currants. We had made a great effort to personalize the creature and now she was no more. However, any sense of loss soon passed for I was still in awe of the miraculous transformation that had taken place.

The silk ball was put away in the school's glass-fronted museum cupboard and we were asked to write down what we remembered about the operation. I described the selfless act of the friend who made it possible for me to enjoy 'an experience I would treasure for the rest of my life'. Miss Thomas will have thought I meant the part I played in the unravelling of the silk. Walter, who knew better, summed up the episode nicely:

'Yew lucky bugger,' he whispered in my ear as we came out through the school gates.

'Thanks, Walter,' was all I could say.

Chapter Twelve

There was an abundance of countryside fruits due to the recent rains that followed the long dry spell and we were determined to bring in a good harvest. My mother had already gathered fifteen pounds of blackberries and most of them were now in preserving jars on our cold pantry shelf. Picking sloes, however, was man's work, or at least a job for adventurous boys. This year the fruit hung invitingly in huge blue-black clusters, some sloes almost as big as damsons.

Walter and I set off to the woods with my father's sickle and a jute bag. The blackthorn tree doesn't yield willingly to human marauders, but an hour later we returned with about ten pounds of hard-won fruit. The shortage of sugar had led to a curtailment of wine-making in the village, but those families like ours who had saved their rations for the purpose had got their priorities right. Wine wasn't the countryside's only bounty, though, for Walter and I were soon amongst the trees again, gathering crab-apples to make that sweet-sour jelly which would enliven coarse wartime bread and turn fatty fried bacon into a delicacy fit for emperors. Walter's mother wouldn't have the time or the inclination to make such luxuries, so the fruit he picked came to us and our Mam would see to it that Mrs Hopkins would be well supplied with tasty spreads at Christmas.

Thus was Saturday spent and Walter and I felt proud of our good deeds, albeit we were tired and sorely pricked. We sat on our back doorstep, lying to each other as we competed for the larger number of alleged thorny penetrations to hands, arms, and legs. I led with twenty-seven to his twenty-two, until Walter claimed he found a group of five in one of his legs . . . We settled for an honourable draw.

*   *   *

It was time for a visit to our cousins in Llantrisant, the ancient village sitting on a hill to the west. One morning, after a good seven o'clock breakfast, Gareth and I set off jauntily with our mother on the five-mile walk. The air was crisp and the banks of Tyncoed Lane were damp jungles of dock, burdock, and cow-parsley. The sun was low in the sky and each time we stopped for an occasional look back we would see a dramatic change in the scenery. The banks were alight with gossamer, reflecting the early sunshine and sparkling with droplets of dew. We turned sharply as Gareth pointed and shouted, '*Cadno!*' There was a flash of chestnut-red as the fox darted through milky sunbeams and disappeared up the bank about twenty yards away on the other side of the lane.

'*Dewch! Bryswch!*' said my mother sharply. 'We must get a move on now. If we keep stopping we'll never get there.'

I could never understand why we had to hurry, for even at a slow pace we would be at my great-aunt's house long before mid-morning. On the other hand it occurred to me that the sooner we arrived, the sooner we would get some of my aunty's famous gooseberry tart with the top of the milk and the sooner we would be down at the park where they had slides, round-abouts, and swings – the furniture of heaven.

By the time we came out of Tyncoed forest and made our way up the railway embankment on the last lap of our journey my new shoes were giving me agony. Mam let me take them off on condition I would step only on the sleepers until we left the railway. This I gladly did, then I tried to race my brother until the ominous *choof-choof-choof* of an approaching train obliged the three of us to step down the bank. The engine passed, leaving us with the *gottagetton – gottagetton – gottagetton* of carriages going over rail-joints. The train was packed with soldiers in uniform and I wondered where they might be going. I also wondered if they were Belgians. Not for the first time I promised myself I would ask Walter what he meant by his frequent references to them.

We arrived just after eleven at the house of my grandmother's sister. Bopa Morfydd was fat, jolly, talkative, and powered by a need to stuff everyone around her full of food. Three of her daughters were also there. Our mother joined them at the large table, quickly followed by my great aunt, a large plateful of seedcake, and an enormous teapot. The cousins were all married and living near their mother. Their children, my second cousins, were twelve in number, but three of them were away in the war. Noises from the field behind the house suggested that several of the younger ones had come with their mothers. One of the boys, Maelgwyn, who was my age, rushed into the house to ask breathlessly if I had arrived.

I needed no encouragement to go with Mal. I welcomed the chance to escape the tea-drinking and the gossip about recipes, pregnancies, and the price of food. My brother would always politely stay for a while, gallantly enduring questions about school and what he wanted to be when he grew up and so on before easing himself away to see his younger cousins. No doubt Gareth would join the noisy game of cricket that was going on between our relatives and a number of local lads. I imagined he would arrive in time to save an innings, which is what he often did.

Meanwhile Mal and I would be on our way to the banks of the River Clun to find a suitable place for a chat.

'There's a lot of noise going on back there for a Sunday, Mal.'

'Same as any other day,' he said.

'Not if you lived in Pengarth.'

'Don't they play cricket on Sundays up there, then?'

'Not likely! I said. 'They don't play anything on Sundays. Apart from harmoniums.'

Mal opened the canvas satchel he'd been carrying and produced a bottle of Tizer and two hunks of his grandmother's gooseberry tart, one of which he passed to me.

Said Mal, between munches and gulps: 'Pengarth's a backward place altogether, isn't it! I mean, there's not much *there* is there?'

'Yes, of course there is!'

'All right, what about gas. You got gas up there?'

'No.'

'Railway? Got a railway?'

'No.'

'Electricity?'

'Some.'

The argument was not unfriendly, for Mal and I liked each other. They were a bright lot, my cousins, most of them doing exceptionally well in school. Mal was the only one who shared my disregard for desk learning. He seemed to be my equal in every way and therefore difficult to argue with. It was time, though, for the pendulum of debate to swing in my favour.

'Got a searchlight base?' I asked him.

'Er, no.'

'Anti-aircraft guns?'

'Um, no, of course not.'

The exchanges went on until I decided to bring out my trump card. 'Does the most beautiful girl in the whole world live here in Llantrisant?' I asked, feeling the blush warming my cheeks.

'Ah – ah,' said Mal, smirking. 'I thought there was some-thing different about you. You've found that you like girls!'

I wanted to explain that this was not strictly true. It was only *one* girl that I 'liked' and she happened to be unique. I still thought most other girls could talk only of dolls and dresses, couldn't climb trees, ruined games of football, and were useless at playing 'Fox and Hounds'.

'Let's go to the park,' I said in an attempt to change the subject.

Mal had me on the ropes and he might now go for the knock-out punch; or so I thought. Instead, he got up to his feet and said, 'Well, cousin, I've got the same problem.'

We made our way to the public park, comparing our feelings and experiences. The object of Mal's admiration was a farmer's daughter, named Eiluned.

Alongside each other on the swings we continued our con-fessions and I felt glad to have found someone to whom I could talk openly.

We moved to an iron turntable and as it revolved we dis-cussed an aspect of our plight that had haunted both of us. It was the fact that neither Annabel nor Eiluned, apart from the odd smile, had ever given any indication of liking *us* all that much.

That subject duly exhausted, each of us used a foot to slow the turntable. I stepped off and Mal asked if I felt sick. 'And you're the one who's always wanted to be a sailor!' he added. In fact I was laughing because of something that had suddenly come to mind.

'Share it then, Ger, for God's sake,' said Mal.

'Well, I was just thinking what my friend Walter would have said if he was here now.'

'Oh yeah, what would that be, then?'

'He'd have said: "That's how life's supposed to be, innit. All swings and soddin' roundabouts!"'

My brother called us and we returned to the house. A fine meal was made from scanty rations augmented by produce from Bopa's garden that was worked by a couple of her sons-in-law. Cousins of all ages prepared the food with military precision. Some buttered bread, some sliced boiled beetroot, some washed lettuce and radish. Another laid the table with a spotless white cloth and gleaming cutlery, while Bopa Morfydd supervised the whole affair with matriarchal authority from her chair in the corner of the room. Occasionally she would reach out a chubby arm and hug a grandchild as it passed. Great nephews had the same treatment: she pressed me into her soft mountainous body and with a loving chuckle bent her head to speak into my ear.

'I've got something wonderful to tell you,' she whispered in Welsh.

'Ah, this is it,' I thought. Mal must have been gossiping to her and I'm about to get some advice from his grandmother about affairs of the heart.

'Yes, indeed,' she went on, giving me another squeeze. 'If you're a good boy you can have another helping of gooseberry tart!'

The sun was setting behind us as we approached the edge of *Tyncoed* forest. Ahead, giant beeches and oaks at the top of the ridge were becoming as one with the darkness of the sky. As we entered the forest the air cooled and heady scents of pine mingled with sweet and sour smells that rose from tangled foliage on the damp forest floor. We had chosen a little-used track as a short cut to make up for our late departure and last year's fall of larch needles made for a springy path beneath our feet. The deeper we penetrated the gloom, the night sounds of the woodland became more apparent. Up in the trees various members of the crow family were not yet ready to settle down and were squawking away as they usually did at this time.

For a while we were guided by fading images of ferns and brambles that lined the path. Soon these dissolved into blackness and we were 'lost'.

We came to a stop, regretful at our not having taken the long lane, but it was both too late and too difficult to turn back. I had little doubt that we would be entrapped until dawn by the soot-black night and become prey to the terrors of the forest. Our mother held us close and I felt her faintly tremble as she uttered a brief and almost inaudible prayer.

Gareth eased himself away from Mam's grip. 'Don't worry' he said, firmly, 'I'll find a way out of here.'

I wondered if his words sounded more convincing to our mother than they did to me.

'You stay here with Geraint. I'll find the path again,' said my brother. 'I know this wood well.' As he moved away he added: 'I won't go too far and I'll keep calling you. And I'll need *you* to call back.'

We could hear Gareth's movements through the under-growth, about twenty or so yards away as he circled us. Now and again he would shout, *'Dyma fi,'* 'Here I am,' and we would answer.

Eventually he called out that he had found the path and asked us to make our way carefully towards him. My mother tripped over something and fell with a cry. Manfully I helped her to her feet, but soon I too stumbled over a tree-root and was suddenly a boy again.

We reached the path and were very glad of the friendly feel of larch needles beneath our feet.

'This way,' said Gareth, gently taking Mam's arm and moving to our right. I followed, attached to my mother.

'How do you know this is the right way?' asked Mam after we had taken a few paces.

'Just trust me,' said Gareth.

We plodded on, making sure we kept to the path, and my thoughts sprang to the future wherein my brother would be a great expedition leader. I envisaged the headline: *'Welshman Gareth Llewellyn, the world's greatest explorer, rescues battalion of soldiers in Amazonian jungle!'*

I stopped fantasising upon hearing sounds of grunting and shuffling among the trees somewhere off to the left. My mother tightened her grip on my arm but she relaxed when my brother said: 'Badgers, it's only badgers.'

At last we came out of the wood and paused for a rest at a gate alongside Tyncoed Lane. Seeing the open sky again should have been a relief but the criss-crossing of searchlight beams again brought to mind far greater dangers than those of the forest. The crows had gone to roost and there was silence everywhere. From the direction of Pengarth however, came a mysterious sound. Curiously poignant, it rose and fell in the distance like the song of a skylark on a windy day. There was no apparent movement in the air, yet the sound came wafting over the hedgerows as if on a gentle breeze. It came ever nearer as we stood at the gate. There was a sharp incline in the lane ahead and the nearing sound drew our glances upwards, and as we looked towards the source of the sound we saw a small cluster of tiny lights which seemed to dance their way over the brow of the hill. By now the sound was melodious: euphonious trills and legato notes seemed to emanate from the bobbing lights. Was this the dreaded *Jac y Lantarn*, the ghostly 'Wil o the Wisp' that presaged miseries and even death for some? Hardly, I thought, for we were not on marshy ground. It soon became obvious that the sound was that of a human voice. I recognized both the tenor voice and the song, the words of which were now clear: *'O na fyddai'n haf o hyd,'* 'Oh that it were ever summer' in an experienced tenor voice.

'It's your father!' said Mam, dashing towards the approaching figure. Gareth and I raced after her as the Welsh gave way to

136

the English. *'Red sails in the sunset, red sails on the sea . . . Oh bring back my loved one, home safely to me.'*

After kissing our mother he hugged us before removing his trilby, around the rim of which were a dozen glow-worms he had taken from the bank. The sudden movement dimmed them, for that was their way, but they had done their job.

'You were much later than I'd expected, so I thought I'd come and look for you,' said my father. 'But you really shouldn't have gone – there could have been an air-raid.'

'I wasn't alone,' retorted Mam. 'I had two brave boys with me.'

My brother was getting into his bed as I fixed the blackout sheet. 'Tell me,' I said, as casually as I could, for I was desperate to know. 'How did you find the way out of the wood?'

'Simple,' said Gareth, 'I knew that the roadway was to the south so all I had to do was to find any smooth-barked beech and feel around for the moss which always grows on the north side. It's all in the Scouts' Handbook.'

'Yes,' I said, 'but how did you then find the woodland path so quickly?'

'Instinct,' said Gareth. 'Just instinct.'

What a brother!

Chapter Thirteen

Uncle Dai Lee's two-wheeled cart stood in the lane at the back of our terrace with a high and heavy load that looked as if it would tilt and lift Bonni off the ground if she dared move. For twenty-five years the old cob mare had hauled fruit and vegetables about the parish, occasionally doubling as a furniture remover.

My uncle assured us that Bonni was capable of pulling much heavier loads than ours and indeed when at last the wheels rolled we could see that the horse was coping well. The load trembled a couple of times over stones, but my father and uncle Dai with help from Mr Smitherham had strapped the items on firmly. Our large oak table sat neatly over the sideboard, leaving room at the sides for chairs. Looking undignified lying face down atop the lot was our Welsh dresser, as though resentful at being moved from the cottage where it had stood for three generations. As we left the lane it was Uncle Gwilym's turn with *his* cart and Owain Glyndŵr between the shafts. He and Gareth would bring the second load.

The previous week we had been given the key to our new abode and three days to vacate the old home. My mother had insisted on scrubbing every inch of the council house before moving a 'stick of furniture' out of our old cottage. It was not that the place was grubby, it was just our mother's way. Her motto might have been: 'If it doesn't move, scrub it; if it does move, catch it and *then* scrub it!'

I held Bonni's bridle as the cart trundled along, not because she needed a guide, but because it made me feel good. Her shiny coat was the colour of conkers or the bracken-covered Garth in autumn. The old saddle-backed creature was known to everyone in the village and I gloried in the fact that she belonged to a relative of mine.

My uncle was obliged by the presence of Mr Smitherham to speak English to my father as we walked, although he would suddenly switch to Welsh when giving an occasional instruction to Bonni. This was because the horse's understanding of English was abysmally poor, albeit conceivably better than that of its owner.

'Against we get there now,' said Uncle Dai, using an idiom that lost a shade or two of meaning in the translation and obviously baffled Mr Smitherham, 'there will be great dryness on her.'

'Yes, indeed,' said my father, 'Bonni *will* be thirsty when we arrive.'

'Ah, I see,' said the Englishman, clearly appreciating Dad's role as interpreter.

As the load wobbled its way down Temperance Road curtains moved and faces appeared at some windows, while in a few doorways people stood and shouted good wishes as we passed. Dear old Bopa Angharad, elegant in her black satin dress, still mourning the loss of three husbands long since gone, always called out the same words: 'Let God go with you' whenever anyone went past her house. More often than not she failed to finish her entreaty for her dentures had a habit of leaping from her mouth when she spoke.

My father recognised the intended message and thanked her courteously: *'Diolch, Bopa,'* 'Thank you.' As we moved on I turned and saw that she was already searching the grass around her black-laced-boots.

On arrival at the semi-detached house which was to be our new home, two strong men, friends of my father, waited to help us unload. My mother, who had gone earlier took com-

139

mand of the operation, cheerily giving instructions as to where this, that, or the other, should go. Bryn and Cled, with the grunts of men used to hard labour, introduced the furniture piece by piece to its new home.

I wandered upstairs and went into each of the three bedrooms in turn. Walking around a stately home couldn't have thrilled me more. The rooms were large and airy and smelt of the freshness imposed on them by my mother. Gareth and I would have separate bedrooms and, as I had already been told the one at the back was for me, I went to check it out. Although the view from its window wasn't of our marvellous mountainside, it was just as beautiful in its own way. I would now look southward to the Vale where the county of Glamorgan extended to the coast twelve miles away in a rich spread of pastures dotted here and there with shady copses, hamlets, and spired churches. Beyond the greens and browns of the coastal fields was the strip of silver known to us as *Y Môr Hafren*, The Severn Sea. I could just make out a convoy of half-a-dozen or so merchant ships slowly edging their way past the Steep Holm, a rocky island whose partly Viking name evoked thoughts of the troubled times of long ago. The ships were heading for their own trouble, for they were moving westward to the Atlantic where, I presumed, German submarines would be lying in wait beneath the waves.

I walked into the bathroom and stood before the handbasin, staring at the taps marked 'H' and 'C'. Leaning over the side of the bath I ran my hand across its smooth shiny surface. Again, two taps seemed to be asking to be turned. The availability of water from four outlets, all within a yard of each other under a dry roof, was to me the luxury of the high-born, the unattainable stuff of dreams.

I gripped the hand-basin tap marked 'C' and gave it a turn. Water spurted and, cupping my hands under the stream, I rinsed them and splashed my face, repeating the exercise half-a-dozen times. There was no wind whistling through the gully and no rain machine-gunning the slates above my head.

Aside the bath a seat fit for kings beckoned and I surveyed it in some awe. I had used such contraptions only on visits to the cinema and the doctor's house. There would now be no more sprinting through the storms and fretting as to whether it was possible to make it to the shed in time. There would be no flaking whitewash, no lurking spiders, and no piles of firewood smelling of the damp forest. Here was a shiny oil-clothed floor and tiled walls and a gadget for holding rolls of soft paper when it became available again. This was heaven!

Seven journeys were made before the last item was put into place in our new home.

Extreme care was taken with the last load for it consisted of our piano and our books. There were smiles though when 'The Fall of The House of Usher' fell from the cart. Then one of the wedges holding the piano in place was dislodged and some notes were sent out like the introduction to a song which both my father and my Uncle Dai recognised instantly. Together they burst forth in harmony: *'Trumpeter, what are you sounding now?'*

Finally my father locked the door of the old cottage and took the key to Mr Rhys, the rent collector; and my mother went up to cry in her new bedroom.

'Yew'll still talk to me now that yew live in a posh 'ouse, 'on't yew?' said Walter after I'd given him a guided tour around our new home.

'I might,' I said, matching his mood. 'Especially if you call me "Sir" from now on.'

He hit me harder than he had probably intended, but the force of the blow was taken on the snake-buckle of my belt.

Walter yelped and whirled a couple of times, sucking his knuckles.

'That'll teach you not to strike a member of the gentry!' I called after him as he went off home.

Walter paused at the gate at the end of the Refail lane and I was pleased to see him grinning broadly.

'See yew after tea!' he shouted with a wave. 'Important business, see!' he added, pointing to the mountain.

I remembered then that we had talked of going with some of our evacuee friends on a trip into forbidden territory. We had been challenged by a group who claimed to be the most daring in the school. Their exploits had included removing every strawberry from Eaglebeak's garden and remaining 'innocent' albeit receiving some fierce glares from the headmaster. However, the escapade on which we were about to embark was of Olympian standard by comparison and I felt uneasy about it. We would be required to enter the searchlight and artillery camp on the mountain unchallenged, to make our presence known, and to return with proof of our visit. Reckless!

Even Denzil Matthews, a known daredevil, said, 'You won't catch me goin' up there, mun! They've got machine guns that'll mow you down like corn if you go near 'em.'

There had been gasps of mock disbelief when Walter had said 'Pappsy, mun! Easy! I'll pick a team to do it before the month is out.' We hadn't realised that he was serious.

'Where are you going in such a hurry?' asked Mam, after I had eaten my meal in record time.

'Out.'

'Out's a big place; I've heard of it but where exactly is it?' asked my mother. She stood in the doorway, blocking my exit.

'Well, it moves around,' I said, trying to be clever.

'All right, but where would "out" be today, then?' She folded her arms.

'Up the mountain,' I said, and tried to dive past her. She grabbed me and gave me a hug.

'Well don't go near the army camp,' she said as she stepped aside to let me go. 'They might shoot you!'

'They're on *our* side, Mam, didn't you know?'

As I skipped down the path I could see that my father was turning over the back-garden soil ready for planting spring cabbage. I closed the gate quietly so as not to disturb him and more importantly not to have to tell him where I was going, for without doubt he would have forbidden it.

Walter was waiting for me at the stile alongside the Rest Centre with the rest of the press-ganged team: the Terenzi twins and Peter Lawton. My eye caught what appeared to be a brown paper bag tucked into my best friend's shirt.

'What's in the bag?' I asked, but received no reply.

Walter nodded towards the Garth Mountain stretching above us and said, 'OK, let's get going. We'd better be back down by 'ere before it gets dark.' He slipped down from the stile and immediately set a quick pace.

'You must be the fastest cripple on one-and-a-half legs,' said Mike Terenzi, knowing that Walter never really got upset about references to his deformity. We were half-way up the mountain before Walter reacted to the comment and even then it was more to do with our failure to keep up with him rather than the insult itself. His words were aimed at the heavy Italians.

'Yew may be twins *now*,' he said. 'But if yew don't keep up with me yew'll be soddin' triplets by the time I've finished with yew!'

I thought it was time to repeat my question. 'What's in the bag, Walter?'

'It'll be yewer bloody 'ead, if yew ask me that again,' he said, glaring at me, but also giving a semblance of a wink.

As we approached the highest part of the ridge we could hear voices from the army camp and the sound of moving vehicles.

There was no perimeter fence to worry about – just the risk of being seen.

By now the Terenzis were puffing hard.

'For Christ's sake,' whispered Walter, 'if yew 'ave to breathe at all, do it quietly or we'll all end up in the soddin' glass'ouse!'

I had no wish to be sent to a military prison at my tender age so I thought about deserting our little group there and then. By the look on Peter Lawton's face he too had considered dropping out. The Terenzis were soon breathing normally again but they also appeared as if they would need little persuading to return home. But it took only a couple of words from Walter to restore our resolve to go on:

'Bloody cowards!' he said, staring at each of us in turn. 'Are yew bloody with me or agin me?'

We bowed our heads. '*With* you of course, Walter.' He was our officer and if he was going to lead by example we were duty bound to follow him 'over the top'.

We continued along the cart road which had been used to and from the burial sites on the mountain in prehistoric times. Images of oxen and skids, chariots and sweating horses came to mind and I wondered what the ancients would have made of the vehicles of modern warfare that had lately gone up that same road.

We left the path and although the bracken was dying it still provided good cover as we neared our destination, now only fifty yards away. Peering over the top of the ferns we could see a sentry standing by a small hut against which three rifles were leaning. The guard looked friendly enough; which could not be said of the two creatures which stood on the track twenty yards nearer our position. The pair were sniffing the air and looking in our direction.

'Alsatians!' squeaked Peter Lawton. 'That's buggered it!'

'Nah,' said Walter with a huge grin, 'I'll look after the bloody Alsatians.'

'But I think they can smell us,' whispered Mike Terenzi.

'Course not!' retorted Walter, removing the brown paper parcel from his shirt-front and unwrapping it. 'These are what the buggers want.' He held up two thigh bones of a sheep and, reaching out, pressed them into our hands for a brief moment. The bones, which still bore traces of meat, felt cold and sticky.

'Don't worry,' said Walter, 'the dogs will like yew, now. Mind that yew stay by 'ere till I get back.'

He crawled away on his belly as did Sergeant York on his way to toss grenades into German gunposts. 'Christ,' I thought, 'I hope he's not going to do anything silly.' Two minutes later he was back with two friendly canine companions.

We sat in a small clearing in the bracken to discuss our next move. It was necessary to raise our voices slightly above the sounds of sucking and bone-gnawing from our two new friends.

'Sooner or later that sentry is going to notice that the dogs are missing. That's when we make our move,' said Walter.

We had no idea where we were going or what we were supposed to do when we got there; we just had unlimited faith in our leader. As Walter was speaking he was looking in the direction of the sentry and he suddenly gave us a 'thumbs up'.

We leapt away, but the dogs showed no interest in following us. The soldier was walking towards the clearing and calling out the dogs names repeatedly: 'Captain, Captain, Captain . . . Buller, Buller, Buller . . .'

By the time the guard reached the dogs we were already behind his hut hiding between two water barrels. There was a line of half a dozen or so huts only a short dash apart and each time Walter gave the 'all-clear' we crouched and ran from one to the other until we were well inside the camp. A few soldiers were walking about but none saw us.

At the ridge's highest point in the centre of the complex was the largest of four Garth Mountain burial sites, a Bronze Age round barrow which had dominated the northern horizon for four thousand years.

We lay hidden in the evening shadows behind a wattle-and-clod structure from which an unmanned Lewis gun protruded through a discreet hole facing the southern approach to the camp. The base of the ancient monument was only yards away and Walter whispered that getting to the top of the mound would complete the first part of the challenge. The way my legs were trying to turn me towards home didn't encourage me to think that we would succeed, but once again Walter's leadership prevailed.

'When I do this,' he said, giving his familiar 'thumbs up' sign, 'yew follow me . . . an' when we get there stay stock still.'

'Would you ruddy believe it.' The guard was speaking to his companion. 'Them dogs fahnd some old bones darn there in the bracken. Can't do a bleedin' fing wiv 'em nah.' His accent was similar to that of our first evacuees so I assumed he was from the south-east of England.

The other soldier who had two stripes on his arm was holding an oil can in one hand and a rag in the other. 'Yeah, some bleedin' guard-dogs *they* turned out to bleedin' be,' he said with the same accent. 'Good job we're not expecting trouble, eh?'

He stepped inside the little clay-and-hazel hut and started attending to the gun, while the sentry walked back to his post, whistling happily.

Walter's fist and thumb rose above the skyline and in seconds we were racing up the side of the mound on all fours.

During five minutes that seemed like five hours several soldiers came near the foot of the mound, but not one looked upwards. Lying motionless, we watched various activities with the interest of a fox that has just seen a pack of hounds down in the valley, the only difference being that sooner or later we would have to give ourselves up in order to comply with the terms of the challenge.

Two soldiers were polishing the huge lens on one of the searchlights and each looked our way a couple of times.

The sentry appeared from behind the first hut, stretching his arms and yawning. I heard our leader draw breath and I knew the moment had come for more action. The only parts of Walter that moved were his cheek muscles as he twisted his face to speak from the side of his mouth.

'Leave this to me,' he said, and his tone left no doubt about his seriousness. I guessed he was going to have to get the attention of the guard to prove that we had given ourselves up rather than having been captured.

Despite my great faith in Walter I hoped that he wouldn't choose this moment to do something rash or even suicidal.

I guessed there was some gritting of English and Italian teeth and I could sense the evacuees' tension when Walter got up. The words he called to the sentry seemed to herald the end of our world.

'Hey, Baldy! Heil Hitler!' he shouted. 'Would yew like some more bones for yewer dogs?'

It was the speed with which the guard reached for one of the rifles leaning against the shed and fired it in the air that really caused us to panic. Too grown-up to cry . . . and, I thought with a shudder, too young to die . . . Four young pals, humbled by fear and self-pity, fell and rolled out of control down the eastern flank of the mound, while our brazen leader calmly and slowly *walked* down. When we came to a halt I could see the sentry making his way towards Walter, his gun at the ready.

I tried to shout 'Don't shoot!' but no sound emerged. I tried to get up, but my legs refused to move. Peter Lawton was crossing himself and the Terenzis were muttering something that sounded like Latin.

As the guard came over to him Walter stood there with his hands on his hips, smiling broadly. I felt a huge surge of admiration for him, but I was also fearful for what was going to happen next.

Anxious and excited voices were raised and suddenly a big, strong hand gripped the back of my belt and lifted me clean off the ground. The smell of oil identified my captor as the corporal in charge of the Lewis gun. He, like some others, had raced to the mound in response to the warning shot. At least the feeling had come back to my legs, for although the action was to no avail, I was kicking like a donkey. Messrs. Lawton and Terenzi were being carried in similar fashion until the four of us were unceremoniously dropped onto a patch of turf behind one of the huts.

'Sty on the grahnd and don't move!' said one of the soldiers. 'Sarge'll be along in a minute to tell us what to do wiv ya . . . and Gawd 'elp ya, cos 'e dahnt loike kids wann little bit!'

Although Walter in the meantime had complied with an order to put his hands above his head, he was still smirking when he was brought to join us.

'OK, you can put your 'ands dahn nah,' said the soldier. 'And for Christ's syke stop smoilin' will ya. You give me the bleedin' creeps!'

One or two more soldiers arrived. The sounds of our arrest had interrupted one of them while he was shaving in a nearby tent and he emerged with a faceful of soap.

'Well, what have we here, then?' he said, addressing the corporal but looking at us. 'Germans, are they, Corporal? Well, well, five Germans, eh! What a catch!'

As he turned back to his tent he shook his head. Soap-suds flew from his face and floated away on the rising breeze like tiny clouds. 'God knows what Sarge will do to them when he gets here. Oh-dear-oh-bloody-dear!'

148

We weren't allowed to talk to each other; instead we had to listen to a continuing litany of indications of what 'Sarge' might do to us.

A vehicle approached and stopped in front of us. The three soldiers squatting close-by leaped to their feet, rifles in hand, and saluted the officer who alighted from the open-topped army car. His shoulder-pips identified him as a major. 'My God!' I thought. 'Now we're for it!'

The officer casually returned the salute before coming over to bend down for a close look at us. His right hand held a short, leather-covered swagger stick

'Well this *is* a dangerous looking bunch I must say. Germans, no doubt! Jolly good work! Well done, men! Sergeant Davies will think it's his birthday, what? Ha-ha-ha!' Grinning hugely the officer returned to the car and gave the nod to the driver. As the car disappeared in an easterly direction, another vehicle approached from the west.

The soldiers near us recognised Sergeant Davies when he was still some way off. The reaction to the NCO's arrival was surely of the kind usually reserved for gods and headmasters. He stood upright in the back of the Bren-gun carrier and men were disappearing as the vehicle approached. Those near us were shaking their heads, whistling through their teeth, and giving us grave looks. The sergeant had the straightest back I'd ever seen and it didn't bend an inch as he stepped down from the vehicle. He, too, was carrying a short stick, but whereas the major had used it as a plaything, Sarge had his tucked tightly in his armpit.

The hum of voices stopped precisely the moment the Bren-gun carrier's engine was switched off and an eerie quietness prevailed. Now the only sound was that of a lone skylark that was winging its way to the safety of the clouds. My dread of what might happen next is indescribable. What awful punishment awaited us? There was a shuffling noise and a clicking of heels as the dozen soldiers around us stiffened.

'Stand!' said the monster. We stood.

'Attention!' he shouted, and we immediately obeyed.

He walked up and down in front of us. 'Germans, eh?' he said, turning aside to spit. 'My God, they're sending 'em young these days. This is embarrassing, you know. Our unit's first prisoners of war turn out to be boy soldiers! Never mind, beggars can't be choosers I suppose!'

He stopped his to-ing and fro-ing. Removing his cane from its armpit sheath he used it to tilt Peter Lawton's cap. 'Haircut, you,' he rasped. 'You've got long hair for a bloody German!'

'Yessir,' said the evacuee. 'That's right, sir.'

'And you, and you, and you, and you!' he blasted to the rest of us.

'Yessir,' answered the five voices together.

'Can't 'ave long-'aired prisoners, can we!'

'No, sir.'

'Now, then,' he continued, more calmly, 'you could be taken from here to a prison camp where you'd spend the rest of this war working like slaves. You would toil so 'ard you'd wish you'd never been born!'

I wanted my mother badly.

'Names! From the left!'

'Lawton'. 'Terenzi'. 'Terenzi'. 'Llewellyn'. ''Opkins'.

'Ah, very clever that, pretending not to be Gerries! Just one Saxon, two Wops, and a couple of Taffies!' said the sergeant, and for the first time I looked at his face. Beneath an enormous black moustache was a broad smile which vanished suddenly when he saw me gazing at him.

'No, Sir,' said Walter, 'We're Belgians.' Oh, here he goes again, I thought. God help us!

'You're as Belgian as my arse,' said Sarge. 'How did you get in 'ere? How did you get past our dogs?' At that very moment

150

I felt my hand being licked and glancing down I nearly jumped. The two Alsatians were sniffing at all five of us in turn. Walter had thought of everything.

'I don't get it,' said the guard-duty soldier, shaking his head. 'Those two brutes are trained to kill, and just look at 'em nah!'

'Well, 'ey *are* German Shepherd dogs after all, see. P'raps they recognise their own kind!' Oh, Christ! Walter was pushing his luck again.

'You'd all be shot if I 'ad my way,' said Sergeant Davies. 'But they won't allow that these days. War's not the same since that ruddy Geneva Convention. We'll just 'ave to think of somethin' else, won't we.' He stood looking at the sky and stroking his chin. My legs were shaking again. Peter was sniffling and the Terenzi twins were finding it hard to breathe. The incredible Walter was standing as straight as his game leg would allow, brave as ever, and wearing his most defiant smirk.

'Aw, Goddammit, take 'em away before I think of some 'orrible torture,' said the sergeant suddenly. I could have sworn I saw that smile again as he turned from us. What did it mean?

Escorted by two armed privates we were marched away and pushed into one of the tents. The man we had seen shaving was sitting at a kind of card-table on which were various papers, files, and books.

'German prisoners, Sir!' said one of the privates as he handed us over. 'They're all yours now, Sir. We have to get back to our work, Sir.'

Our new guardian got up and introduced himself as something that sounded like Lieutenant Jeremy Krankenfahrt.

'It's your lucky day, boys. That's what it is – your *lucky day*!' Despite the emphasis I remained unconvinced. I was wretched and desperate to be home in our new council house with my brother doing his homework at the table, my father listening to ITMA on the wireless, and Mam darning socks by the fire.

'Oh, yes, it's your lucky day all right,' he went on. 'You've been let off by Sarge and now you've been delivered to me.' He sat down again in his folding wooden chair and leaned over to open a drawer in a small cabinet that stood alongside the table. He took out a cigar box that bore a colourful picture of a Cuban woman on a tobacco plantation. Noting the pretty scene was one way of diverting my thoughts from what I still felt was a highly dangerous situation – for which we had only ourselves to blame.

The man placed the box on the table before him and lowering his voice he said: 'Look, boys, I've got German ancestors myself and I'm going to take pity on you.' He opened the cigar box and taking from it five pieces of polished brass clipped to cards he gave one to each of us.

'Each of you now holds the badge of the Royal Artillery. Regard it as a memento of your visit here. Proof, if you like.' With the last remark he gave a little sniff as to disguise a smile. 'I've signed and dated each of the cards. They're like medals really, eh? Now clear off while there are no guards around!'

We hesitated.

'Well go on, then. There's no-one about.'

Walter opened a tent-flap and peered out. Turning, he said, 'Thank you, Lieutenant Crackandfart,' and led us out. My legs had recovered and I thought maybe a 'Thank you' in German would be appropriate, but the urge to get away overrode it. We left the tent and ran.

The near end of the camp was deserted as we left, but before we came off the mountain we heard the sound of a generator starting up in preparation for some *serious* night work.

We returned to the village early enough not to raise questions at home, but the farcical episode hadn't quite ended. The caper had earned us the title of 'champions' at school and we wallowed in the sweet notoriety. However, there was a twist.

152

My father's visits to the Lewis Arms were very infrequent by this time; he never stayed out late and certainly never became drunk as in the old days. But he was always talkative on his return, as indeed he was on the second night following our adventure. Returning from the bathroom to my bedroom I heard him talking to my mother downstairs. Sounds moved around our new house more freely than they used to in the old stone cottage and from the landing I could clearly hear my father's voice. He was telling Mam that he had been in the company of some off-duty soldiers who related a marvellous tale about some local kids who thought they'd successfully invaded the searchlight and artillery base by fooling the guards.

'Apparently,' chuckled my father, 'the poor kids were frightened out of their wits. They really thought they'd never see their homes and families again!'

'I don't think that's funny,' said my mother quietly. 'I'm just glad neither of our two was up there.'

There were more knots in my stomach than in the Scout Handbook.

'Yes,' said my father, 'but wait till you hear the best bit.'

Although I could hear well enough I instinctively moved down two carpeted steps to make sure I didn't miss what was coming next.

'It seems that it was all set up by the Army men and the Hopkins boy, the one with the game leg. He'd gone up there the week before and planned the escapade with the soldiers right down to the last detail. And would you believe, the boy's mates didn't suspect a thing! He must be a genius, that Hopkins lad.'

Chapter Fourteen

The lady at the door put her ear-trumpet to the side of her head and indicated with a finger that I should speak into its bell.

'Salvage, please, Mrs Edmunds,' I said rather loudly. 'Have you any salvage?'

'Sausage? What do you mean, sausage?'

I held up the Collectors' Information Card and the message got through.

'Oh, it's *salvage* you want! Why didn't you say so, boy?'

Not wishing to appear disrespectful I gratefully accepted a stack of women's magazines from the 1920s. I wondered what they would later be turned into.

We liked to think that we played our part in the war effort and generally felt that the harder we worked, the sooner the conflict would be over. My gang of salvage collectors was led enthusiastically by who else but Walter Hopkins, whose natural humour and charm proved invaluable.

'Excuse me, Mr Evans,' he'd say. 'Could yew please let us have that old kettle? It's for a Spitfire we're building, see.'

'Certainly, my lad. And where exactly are you building the plane?'

Walter would put the tip of his forefinger to the side of his nose and say, 'Can't tell yew, I'm afraid. Top secret.'

Our kettle collection grew impressively.

Bob Forest, a sack merchant living in the village, gave us a lot of hessian bags for waste paper, which, together with the kettles and other metal objects, we took to the collection centre – the garden of one of the large houses in Heol y Parc.

It would be revealed years later that much of the salvage collection had been little more than a propaganda and morale-boosting operation. It is said that the iron railings people surrendered were never recycled for the war machine. Looking back, we should have had doubts about the fate of those kettles, too. One benefit of the exercise was the community spirit that it engendered. The chief organiser Mrs Netta James saw to it that collectors could feel their efforts were appreciated by aranging social evenings and long charabanc trips. I was privi-leged to go on some of these, and, prone to travel sickness, often allowed to stand up front near the driver.

We once went to Aberystwyth, a two-hundred-miles round journey. Because the place was awash with military personnel we had difficulty finding a place to eat. I recall that we went to a chip shop and each of us settled for hake and threepenneth which we took to the promenade to consume. I vividly remem-ber the expression on Daniel Tonmawr's face when a seagull dived and took away his piece of fish. I remember what he said too.

On the way home, in spite of the picturesque mountains and streams around Llangurig, I couldn't help feeling quite home-sick for Pengarth. But soon, and in spite of the almost non-stop singing of popular songs – 'South Of The Border', 'She'll Be Coming Round the Mountain', etc., I fell soundly asleep in the aisle; to awaken as we were climbing the Heol Goch hill to our village.

On another occasion we went to Swansea; only to find it closed – the beach, that is. There was a military exercise in pro-gress, so instead of building sandcastles we sat on the sea wall watching soldiers laying barbed wire across the sands.

A further trip should have had for me a huge advantage over the others, for Annabel was on the bus. However, sitting with Mrs Protheroe in the first seats, she not once turned to acknowledge my presence at the back. Had Peter Blenkinsop not taken my usual place up front near the driver, she would have had no choice but to look at me. Such is fate.

Our first stop was Chepstow Castle, where we had a picnic on the grass in front of the main entrance. Netta James got everyone singing and we were in jolly mood when we left for the next stop, which would be up-river near Tintern Abbey. Before we arrived Gareth stood up and recited Wordsworth's poem about the Abbey and sat down to loud clapping as we pulled into the yard of The Anchor. Alcoholic refreshments were taken by a few, and, although soft drinks were bought for the youngsters, it soon became clear that some of the Chapel folk wanted to get away as soon as possible!

At the small riverside resort of Symond's Yat the river Wye meanders around the Monmouth bluff before joining the Severn estuary twenty miles away. I couldn't believe my luck when I stepped down from the bus, for the next to alight was Annabel. Instinctively I held out my hand to help her down. This moment could have been pivotal – crucial to my romantic fortunes. However, she accepted my hand quite perfunctorily and with a whispered 'Thank you' walked off to join the Protheroes who had gone ahead.

I felt warm breath on the back of my neck. It was Idris Pugh.

'I saw that,' he said. 'Who do you think you are? A knight in shinin' bloody armour?'

I felt like punching his silly face, but, with commendable self-control, I just gave him a big smile and walked away.

Although I counted the incident with Annabel as a slight step forward in my plan to otherwise take the hand of my dream girl, I felt I could have done better. Perhaps I should have walked with her while I had the opportunity.

The Salvage Group's bus-runs weren't the only excursions, for there was also the Sunday School annual outing, with either Barry Island or Porthcawl as the destination. We, the Bronllwyn Congregationalists, would always choose the latter; being further away it meant a longer day out.

This time our Sunday School left for Porthcawl on a Saturday in late September, a month later than usual because the buses of the local firm Phillips and Co. had previously been commandeered for four weeks' wartime work.

Before we were half-way there we were already agog with anticipation of the sea, the sand, and the sunshine. Annabel sat with her brother towards the front of the bus and I was with Gareth at the back. Try as I might, I just couldn't devise a plan that would have contrived a place-swap with Ronnie . . .

Porthcawl had changed. Most of the shows and amusements were boarded up and a pervading greyness made us wistful for the time when the shop-exteriors were a mass of brightly-coloured beach-balls, buckets, and spades. But this was wartime and we had to make the best of it.

The trip went off pleasantly enough, but I could have done without my failure to get close to Annabel. When she paddled in the sea, I paddled in the sea. When she went to watch a Punch and Judy show, I was there too. Every time I approached her I was thwarted by some crude interruption, such as some twit barging in with an inanity that she would politely acknowledge. It did occur to me, though, that if my unhealthy jealousy were to continue I would surely begin to hate myself.

Back in Pengarth I waved goodbye to her, but I don't think she saw me.

As the weather was still reasonable we spent a lot of time outdoors after school and at weekends. The woods were a great attraction, and with our knives and axes we would descend upon Coed y Bedw like a gang of lumberjacks. Birch and alder were felled to make little bridges across the stream. We built barricaded dens from which, we told the younger ones, we could look out for the approach of invading Germans – or a visit from our rivals in Taff's Well, the village down the valley. Of course, neither party ever came.

Had we so wished we could have survived in our woodland retreat for long periods. From the Scouts' handbook we had learned how to make hay boxes for keeping food warm and to adapt biscuit tins that would be miniature refrigerators when placed in the cool waters of the stream.

Wisps of smoke rising from our campfire in a woodland clearing were a common sight. We would be boiling potatoes in a saucepan or baking them black in the body of the fire. Occasionally there would be delightful extras to crown the meals, with tiny trout, tickled from one of the still pools of the Cwmllwydrew brook, undoubtedly our favourite. Cooked by holding them on wire prongs above the flames they were delicious. However, moorhens' eggs, removed in springtime from nests on Cefn Cwtyn pond, were very much an acquired taste.

Our sojourns in the wood were all the more enjoyable for a particular hazard we faced. Climbing trees, playing with axes and fire, were deliciously dangerous, but there was a deep concern that gave us a real frisson. This was the constant fear of being caught by Simpson the Keeper, who roamed the countryside on behalf of the absentee landowner in search of juvenile miscreants. No confrontation between Simpson and grown-up poachers, of whom there were many, was ever recorded, but he often had children taken to court for trespassing on his employer's land. As we were guilty of more than mere trespass, we knew that if we were caught by him severe punishment would surely follow.

It was a glorious Saturday afternoon when it happened. Evacuee Brian Lawton and I had left the campfire to gather more wood. With our axes at the ready we were making our way along a path towards a spot where we knew there'd be some good dry sticks. Something we saw ahead made us stop, suddenly overcome by a sense of foreboding. A large bicycle was leaning against a beech tree, the owner identified in his absence by a twelve-bore shotgun strapped to the bike's bar.

'My God!' I said, ready to run for it, but not sure of which direction to take. 'He must be around here somewhere!'

He was indeed. A heavy hand gripped my shoulder and turned me around to face the gamekeeper's glare. He was bigger than I'd imagined, for I had only ever seen him from a distance.

'*Got you!*' he said. 'You're in big trouble my lad!'

Releasing me, he took a notebook from his jacket pocket. 'What is your name?'

I was shaking with fear, but said nothing. I was now alone, for Brian Lawton had wisely scarpered.

'Give me your name, you little brat,' said Simpson, bringing his head close to mine, 'or I'll beat the living daylights out of you!'

I had no choice, but as soon as I said 'Geraint Llewellyn,' I was surprised to see him take a step back.

'*Llewellyn?*' he said, rubbing his chin. 'Now which of the Llewellyns would that be? What's your father's first name?'

'Rhys,' I said.

His eyebrows rose. 'Don't know him. Are you telling me the truth, boy?'

'Well,' I said, 'Rhys *is* my father's first name, but he does have another: Trefor.'

The gamekeeper stiffened. I imagined his brain working overtime and I began to feel a bit less frightened.

'Do you live down, er, Cambria Lane?' he said, his voice somewhat quieter now.

'Oh, yes,' I answered firmly, confident now that I knew which way his mind was moving.

Although he would undoubtedly have associated Dad with my uncle Twm Lee, the old mountain fighter, and with our friends like the boxing enthusiast Ianto Protheroe, there was another reason for his hesitancy. It was less to do with the possibility of physical retribution than the likelihood of being humiliated once again by an intellectual superior. My father had once spoken on behalf of a group of youngsters who'd found themselves in Whitchurch Magistrates Court after being falsely accused by Simpson of stealing timber meant for pit-prop production. The kids had simply been taking home dead-wood in accordance with an accepted centuries-old tradition of the countryside. On that occasion, at the end of the case, the chairman of the bench had told the gamekeeper to go home, look after his rabbits, and not to waste the Court's time again. 'Well, I'm letting you off on this occasion, Llewellyn,' said the keeper, 'but remember that you were in fact trespassing and I would have every right to bring the law down upon your head. Next time it will be different.' Without further comment he turned away, got on his bike, and rode off.

*　　　*　　　*

One Monday morning we arrived at school and were intrigued to find a large van parked outside. There was no indication of what it contained or why it was there. Our teachers couldn't be persuaded to divulge what it was all about, but we guessed they knew. We were told we would find out soon enough, but we had to be patient. Furthermore, there were priorities. On Mondays the first duty after Assembly was the ritual of collecting War Savings from the pupils. Whenever spare cash became available our parents would allow us to take it to school for the purchase of National Savings stamps. When we'd saved the princely sum of fifteen shillings (75p) we would qualify for a savings certificate that was meant to be kept for ten years, by which time its value would have swollen to £1.5s (£1.25p). There was friendly competition between classes and each room had a savings 'barometer' by which we could compare the growth of our respective funds. The teachers would set targets, which, when reached, caused much excitement.

At last all classes were called again to the main hall for the secrets of the van to be unveiled. The vehicle had delivered something the school had apparently been waiting for since before the war. When we were told that a full set of instruments for a percussion band had been taken from the van and that we could stay to see the boxes opened, a great cheer went up. There were further shouts of approval as each different item was removed from its packing. Because the instruments were of varying appeal, some were applauded more than others. The drum kit brought the loudest acclaim, for we all fancied having a go at that. The cymbals and the tambourines were quite well received, but only a mild response greeted the triangles. It was hard to get excited about a triangle.

Like everyone else, when our percussion lessons started I longed to be allocated a kettledrum and sticks. Fate, however, ordained that I should play the triangle! But it could have been worse: Walter and the Terenzi twins were given castanets.

*   *   *

Before the end of September Pengarth was invaded again. Our school, already almost bursting at the seams, had to accommodate another busload of evacuees, this time from Birmingham. The new arrivals were just as quickly absorbed and despite their different accents and curious speech patterns further strong friendships were formed. There were some pretty girls among them, too, but *my* eyes were for someone else . . . However, even though things had looked promising during our silk-manufacturing episode, I'd still been unable to establish a firm relationship with Annabel. I was determined that sooner rather than later I would do *something* about the situation once and for all. In the meantime, I would continue to enjoy the many pleasant distractions of village life.

Chapter Fifteen

Well before the arrival of the long winter nights, autumn had warned of the cold times to come. At first, on cool and softly-whispering winds, leaves had been gently released and sent fluttering slowly down like tipsy moths. But then chilling gusts came over the slopes of the Garth hill to strip oak and ash, birch and beech, sycamore and chestnut, until they stood stark and naked like the masts of de-rigged sailing ships. Beneath them were the yellows and russet browns of a carpet that not only covered the forest floor, but also filled the lanes about the village, softening the sounds of hoof and footstep until the rains came again and made a patchy mush of it all.

The storm rampaged relentlessly for three weeks, with Nant Cwmllwydrew bursting its banks and turning Tom the Tinker's Meadow into a lake. In our hill village there was a shortage of ponds, so we took full advantage of the flood. On a Saturday morning we would step onto pieces of timber the storm had freed from the wood and turn ourselves into log-riding lumber-jacks. Then we would sail our hastily-made model boats across the rippling waters, their crude sails cut from cast-off shirts straining tautly in the wind. We would return home with water in our boots, but with colour in our cheeks and joy in our hearts.

On other evenings we would assemble at High Corner near Pegler's store and take it in turns to stand with our backs to the outside of the chimney breast of Mari Powell's house. We enjoyed the warmth which permeated the wall that was sheltered from cold winds. The howling gales were exciting to listen to if you were cosy and in no danger. We would gather in a huddle and swap stories which, if Walter was around, would often be not only topical, but rib-cracking.

This time he said: 'Terrible wind, this, innit!' And we knew there was a tale about to be told.

'Aye, Walter,' we replied. 'What about it, then?'

'Well it's dangerous, innit.'

'Aye, Walter, what's happened, then?'

'Well 'aven't yew 'eard?'

'Heard what?'

'Yew know, about Eaglebeak, poor bugger.'

Suddenly we became interested. 'Eaglebeak? *Eaglebeak*?'

'Yeah, our very own Eaglebloodybeak.'

'Come on, Walter! What about him, for God's sake?'

'Well, 'e was walkin' past the school, see, an' a terrible thing 'appened to 'im. 'Honest.'

'*What* happened? Are you going to tell us or not?'

'Well, old Eaglebeak, see, was walkin' past the school when a 'uge slate blew off the roof an' missed the end of his shoulder by about twelve inches.'

'Could have been very nasty, that,' someone said.

'It *was*, mun. It split 'is soddin' 'ead right open!'

When the rain stopped we were well into November. One morning, as it usually did, the sun rose above the Lesser Garth ridge; but shiftily at first, like an intruder. People made jokes, pretending not to know what the bright light in the sky could possibly be. The roads were still glistening when I caught up with Walter on the way to school.

'The Devil's finished piddlin' on us, then' he said. I was struggling to think of a suitable reply when I became aware of something large lumbering behind us. It was Handel Griffiths, nearly out of breath and almost unable to speak.

'What's the rush?' I asked as he came alongside. 'And what have you got in that bag?'

'Oh . . . *pant* . . . this . . . *pant* . . . it's something special . . . *wheeze* . . . I'm taking to school . . . *wheeze* . . . *wheeze.* Everyone will go crazy when they see what it is!'

'Gissa look, 'en,' demanded Walter. 'Can't be anythin' we 'aven't seen before.'

Handel refused, and clutching the bag tightly, turned to go. 'See you in the yard at break time and you'll find out what it is,' he said.

I spent most of the morning doing in class what I usually did, stretching my neck to look across the room at Annabel as often as I could without being noticed. The supplies cupboard was adjacent to her desk and I found myself frequently asking to be allowed to get items: to refill my inkwell or to sharpen pencils so that I could be near her. I hated myself for these sly manoeuvres and for not having the courage to take her aside and declare my love for her properly.

Playtime came and Handel was in the yard standing on a stone plinth that served perfectly as a pulpit. He held his carrier bag high to get everyone's attention. Boots clattered acoss the yard as we were drawn to him like iron filings to a magnet.

'Can anyone guess what I have here?' said Handel.

'It's a bloody carrier bag, innit. Anybody can bloody tell that,' said Idwal James. Everyone laughed. Except Idwal.

'It's what's in it that matters,' said Handel. He called for silence and then drew from the bag something from so far back in our collective memory that we'd stopped thinking about it: a big yellow banana!

If Fatty Griffiths had produced the Koh-i-noor diamond there would have been no greater reaction. Everyone cheered.

Perhaps wartime shortages were having more effect than we knew, for when Handel said that each one of us would get a share of the fruit no one questioned it. Walter slipped down from the wall and joined the orderly queue that had formed according to the wartime code of behaviour. Only Dilwyn barged his way to a forward position in the line, but then he did have a reputation to maintain, so no one objected.

Handel slowly peeled the banana and explained its provenance. 'My Uncle Glyn's ship returned with a convoy from the West Indies yesterday. He gave me this – and I want to share it with you. It was a bit green yesterday but it ripened overnight – just for us!'

Taking a razor-blade from his pocket, he proceeded to slice thin wafers from the banana. With some solemnity each of us was served a slice as the queue moved slowly past the plinth. Handel was like a bishop at Holy Communion and we were the recipients of a great blessing.

The wafers were so meagre that their contact with and effect on our palates turned out to be pitiably brief; so transient in fact that the younger children would still be none-the-wiser as to the taste of the tropical treasure I'd always considered the banana to be.

The queue was still moving when the bell went. I was close to Eaglebeak and Mr Lewis when they stepped out into the yard, open-mouthed at what they saw. The headmaster spoke first.

'No loaves and fishes this time, Mr Lewis,' he said to his colleague. 'Symbolic though, wouldn't you say?'

'Indeed, Mr David. Truly allegorical!' said Mr Lewis. They both smiled, and with some head-shaking they went back into the building.

I turned to see Handel serving the last of his congregation and to hear the final words of the ritual.

'Bugger it!' cried the bishop. '*I* haven't got any!'

*　　*　　*

On the way home from school one day I was collared by Bopa Angharad as I was passing her cottage. She insisted I go inside her home to see something that would ease my way along life's road. It turned out to be 'The Broad and The Narrow Way', a large picture which showed the pitfalls which result from sinful living. She perched her reading glasses on the end of her nose and I knew she would insist on referring to every scene in the picture. I didn't have the heart to explain that I was already very familiar with it as it had hung next to our stairs door in the old house. Twm the Poacher also had one. So did Bopa Mari, Selina John, and Shinco Price. The poster had been distributed in Victorian times by some evangelical group and given free to the purchasers of a brand of soap. It occupied the prime position above the mantlepiece in Bopa's house and close scrutiny of it required standing uncomfortably close to the coal fire.

Lit only by a weak late afternoon sun entering shyly through a tiny lace-curtained window, the picture was bathed in a kind of pious gloom. The devout Bopa, whose eyes sparkled adoringly behind the brass frames of her spectacles, clearly saw it as the word of God in pictures. Despite her scant English and her troublesome dentures, she was able to explain the scenes depicted well enough, inclusive of the book, chapter, and verse references from the Bible that were scattered over the illustration.

In the foreground stands a wall with two entrances from which to choose your route through life. The one on the left leads to the 'Broad Way' and invites you to pass through the gate of Bacchus and Venus, the route of those who seek pleasure before piety and pay for their self-indulgence with eternal punishment. Just inside the gate we see the relevant quotation from Matthew 7, 13: *Broad is the way that leadeth to destruction, and many there be which go in thereat.*

At the end of the road the final destination of the unrepentant burns hot at the top left hand corner (Matthew 25, 41: *Depart from me, ye cursed, into everlasting fire, prepared for the devil and his angels.'*) Just before the inferno, however, a place is retained for the depiction of something so wicked it made Bopa momentarily avert her gaze – the Sunday Train! Bopa belonged to that age when many aspects of modern life were considered offensive to the Sabbath.

The other option is to take the right hand route, entered by a tiny door tucked into the wall, at which point you bid farewell to all worldly pleasures: *'Enter ye at the strait gate.'* Then, along a steep and winding path, we see acts of selflessness, succour, and mercy taking place. At the end of this arduous journey is the Golden City where the Lamb of God stands upon a mount and trumpet-playing angels blow a fanfare of welcome to the latest arrivals who are presumably weary but pure.

'P'un 'rwyt ti wedi dewish ta?' asked Bopa, removing her specs and giving the fire a poke. 'Which route have you chosen?'

'O, 'run sy' ar y dde Bopa, y llwybar creigiog!' 'The one on the right, the rocky path.' And after a suitable pause I added, 'I want to go to heaven, see.'

I dared not tell her what my father had once blasphemously told Mr Smitherham about the picture.

'You see, Smithie,' he'd said, 'there's no reason why you shouldn't choose the Broad Way and get the best out of it until you reach the spot opposite *"the wicked turn from this way and live"*, Ezekiel 33, 11. There you'll see a little gap in the fence that separates the two options. Easy to slip across from there to the Salvation Road! Mind you, Smithie, there's no turning back after *that*!'

Bopa Angharad came to the door with me. 'Let God go with you,' she said as I left. I walked home feeling I'd had quite enough religion for one day.

I was a fully-fledged Scout now, and there were several functions that our troop had to attend in uniform. On the eleventh of November we assembled on the wide road near the parish church, together with the Wolf Cubs, the newly-formed Girl Guides, and the Brownies, in preparation for the solemn procession to the village war memorial in the company of representatives of all the services.

Before the march there was a Scouts' inspection parade. I was in my brother's patrol and felt a twinge of pride when I noticed his exemplary bearing. He walked up and down in front of us like a popular general, adjusting one or two neckerchiefs and woggles and straightening a few hats. He had little to say though, until he came to me.

'Scout!'

'Yessir!'

'You must say "Patrol Leader". Not "sir."'

'Yes, Patrol Leader.'

'New recruit, aren't you?'

'Yes sir, I mean, er . . . Patrol Leader.' I could sense the smiles of the others.

'How do you think a Scout should dress, then?'

'Oh, correctly at all times sir, er . . . Patrol Leader. Er, spick and span. Oh yes, Patrol Leader.'

'Smoothly-ironed shirt and shorts, tidy neckerchief, woggle in correct position, stockings pulled up, and boots polished like mirrors?'

'Yes, Patrol Leader.'

'Nothing else?'

'That's right, Patrol Leader.'

'Sure, now?'

'Yes, Patrol Leader.' Although he was my hero, my brother was beginning to irritate me. 'Is that all, Patrol Leader?' I asked, pushing my luck.

''Fraid not,' said Gareth with a little sniff. 'You've already forgotten why you wanted to join the Scouts.'

'Beg your pardon, sir, I mean Patrol Leader?'

'To wear those little garter tabs you like so much, of course.' Amid raucous laughter he handed me two pieces of green fabric. 'You left them on the kitchen table!' He slapped me gently and proceeded down the rank.

With thoughts of horrible revenge I fitted the tabs and then, glancing across the roadway, I froze. Opposite our group and very much within earshot of what had just taken place stood the party of Girl Guides, among whom was the prettiest girl ever to don a uniform. She was looking straight at me, but when I caught her gaze she turned away enigmatically. I pulled myself together. Why should I concern myself with the meaning of a girl's glance? I was soon to be reminded that there were more important things to be attended to when the Tongwynlais Silver Band started tuning up. The procession would be starting soon and there was serious business ahead.

We formed in marching line just behind the Wolf Cubs and I thought how young they looked, forgetting that not so long ago I had been a member of the same group.

Behind us were the Guides, but because of the solemnity of the occasion I felt it would be disrespectful to even think about looking behind me to seek out Annabel. The band began playing a respectful march and we moved forward in perfect step, the bandmaster in Home Guard Uniform leading the way with the stiff-arm motions of a clockwork soldier. The euphonium player had some trouble keeping in step, but he never missed a note. We marched through the village, past small groups of people watching from the roadside. Without exception the men removed their caps as we went by. Bopa Angharad was outside her cottage calling 'Let God go with you' several times until the last of the line passed her. I didn't dare take a look to see if she was bent over the grass again . . .

We marched to a slow dirge on the remainder of the route and, after arriving at the cenotaph, we stood at attention while a representative of Colonel Westfield, our main absentee land-owner, laid a wreath at the foot of the column. The vicar spoke for five minutes in English and five in Welsh before handing over to Illtyd Probert who did likewise.

Both eulogies referred to the tragedy of the First World War, the horrendous loss of young lives exemplified by the list of names on our own memorial, and the distressing certainty that the present conflict would provide several others. More wreaths were laid and there was a nervous moment for me when my father appeared from behind the cenotaph to stand at attention before it. His shining brass bugle usually rested on our mantel-shelf; only once or twice had he blown it in my presence, and on each occasion he was inebriated. I looked across at my brother, who immediately gave me a nod and a 'thumbs up' – meaning 'Don't worry. He can do it!'

Dad stepped forward and his faultless rendering of 'The Last Post' brought a lump to my throat.

The rest of November remained dry enough for us to introduce the evacuees to the after-dark pursuit of 'Fox and Hounds'. One boy would be chosen as the 'fox' and he would be given fifteen minutes to get away. This was no ordinary 'hide and seek' for it involved courage, strength, fleetness of foot, and frequent mischief.

It bore little resemblance to a real fox-hunt, which had a strong and long-established tradition in Pengarth, but was now suspended for the duration of the war. The 'fox' carried on his person the same object that had been used for many genera-tions: a special 1797 penny which bore the head of George III. It had almost the diameter of a pocket watch and almost the same thickness. The contest was considered won by the fugitive if he was able to evade detection and return the coin to a hole in the wall at the Groeslon crossroads no earlier than 8 p.m. and no later than 9 p.m. When he had returned undetected to any point within earshot of the Groeslon, he was permitted to call 'Cri!' (pronounced 'Cree'). This meant that he could then place the coin with impunity.

We were convinced by stories we'd heard that boys in our grandfathers' time had the advantage of being superhuman. It was said that the twelve-year-old Wil y Gof had climbed up the outside of the church steeple and given the bell a couple of rings before scampering down again and running off with the pack in hot pursuit.

In my own time Walter was by far the best 'fox'. He turned in a magnificent performance on the night the evacuees first joined the game and his chasers were astounded by his stealth, his athleticism, and his cheek. Disguised as a scarecrow he had stood at the edge of Wil Penllwyn's winter cornfield while un-suspecting hunters had passed several times. Most impressive of all was his appearance on a rooftop, taunting his seekers before vanishing. Sore and weary, the pack arrived at the Groeslon at nine to concede defeat. The referee, as always, was the reliable Gwyn Jones, the vicar's son, who confirmed that Walter had strolled up with the penny at exactly one minute to nine!

Usually we would round off our evening with half-an-hour of singing practice at the 'Bardic', a bench near the Twyn mound. The evacuees considered it curious and 'bloody silly' that we should sing outdoors on a cold winter's night, but soon they, too, found it addictive.

Handel Griffiths, our leader, had no doubt inherited much of the musical magic of his grandfather 'Waldo the Wand', a former conductor of three local choirs.

Handel always put newcomers through a quick test, telling this one he was a top tenor, that one a baritone, another a second tenor, and so on. This had come as a great revelation to some of the evacuees, who hadn't previously known that they could sing at all. Personally I had doubts about some of them, but Handel's skill in coordinating the sounds overcame most weaknesses. He always brought his grandfather's baton with him and it gave him an extra air of authority. Passers-by often stopped to listen, clearly happy that a village tradition prevailed.

'MMMMMMMM . . .'

The tenors held their trial note as clear as the ring of a tuning fork.

Then the 'deeps':

'OOOOOOOOO . . .'

It helped that we had in our midst a few fifteen-year-olds whose voices had broken and could now produce a smooth low note.

This night we were at last ready to give it our best. Few pleasures exceed that of making a sweet chord, and, on the lift of the baton, our conductor called for the combination.

In the cold air the breath of a dozen voices vapourised and curled like mist in the light of the street lamp above us. We had to repeat the exercise several times before Handel was satisfied with pitch, volume, tone, and breathing. Then he called for silence with his arm raised and the wand gripped delicately like a quill pen in his plump, mittened hand. We sang two Welsh songs before having a go at a lovely old English Victorian piece on which we had been working for weeks.

'Sometimes between long shadows on the gra–a–a–a–a–a–ass,
The truant rays of sunshine seem to pa–a–a–a–a–a–ss.
My eyes grow dim with tenderness the while . . .
Thinking I se–e–e–e–e–e the–e–e–e–e–e.
Thinking I see thee . . . smile.'

Above us a crescent moon slid out from behind a cloud and we became helplessly intoxicated by our own sweet harmonies. My spirit soared. I felt rapturously romantic. And I longed to be with Annabel.

Chapter Sixteen

My schooldays were definitely happier now that Mary Thomas was my teacher, but I still had problems.

The results of the early winter term tests put up on our classroom wall exposed my meagre scholarship. While I was fairly high up the lists in English and Welsh and was third in Drawing, my record in several other subjects was dismal. It was the bankruptcy of my arithmetic that bothered me most. Yet this time I found my name had risen in that subject to the heady position of second from the bottom. This was noted by Eaglebeak when he came to the classroom to examine the results.

'Llewellyn,' he said, picking out my name with the end of his cane. 'This is a remarkable improvement on last term, if I may say so!' I still had to learn the difference between honest admiration and sarcasm. I blamed my innumeracy on the lack of a clear mind. Some days a whole hour would pass without my thinking of Annabel, but these were the exceptions.

Fortunately I had some distractions: the Silver Screen, my books, my love of the countryside, my interest in the weather. My nightly prayers included thanks for my blissful home life and regular requests for Annabel to be invested with a restless curiosity to know more about that Llewellyn boy with the funny name.

Our monthly visit to the cinema was due and we decided to see the new Hollywood film that everyone was talking about. 'How Green Was My Valley' was the story of a nineteenth century Welsh mining community and based on a book that both my father and my brother had read.

'It'll be a fine picture if it's half as good as the book,' said Gareth, polishing his shoes outside the back door. Mam, my brother, and myself were preparing to take the Saturday morning bus to Cardiff.

'Tell us what it's all about, then,' I shouted impatiently from the kitchen where I was finishing my porridge.

'Can't do that. It'll spoil the film for you,' said Gareth. 'And don't talk with your mouth full!'

I was searching for a suitable retort when I saw a familiar figure go past the window. Before Eaglebeak could knock on the door I was under the table.

Eaglebeak! My God, *Eaglebeak! Coming to our house!* My mother asked the headmaster into the kitchen.

'*Bore da*, Mrs Llewellyn. Good morning. Er . . . I was hoping to find your husband at home.'

'Sorry, Mr David, he works on Saturday mornings. Can I help you?'

'Well, it's about your boy, Geraint. I *do* care about the children, you know. I'm not the tyrant some people think I am.'

'Well, he was about here a moment ago' said my mother. 'But Mr David, please. What *about* him? Is there anything wrong?'

'Well, I'm not sure. Let me put it this way,' said Eaglebeak. 'He's not the bright boy he used to be. He . . . er . . . seems far away all the time and he's got a big exam in the spring. It's in my interest, of course, to get as many as possible to pass, but I am also concerned for the children's sake. Please believe me.'

'I'm sorry you are having trouble with him, Mr David. And there was I thinking he was doing well. Let's see what he has to say for himself. Geraint! Where are you?' I stiffened myself and was pleased to hear my mother continue. 'I am sorry, Mr David, I really can't think *where* he's gone!'

My fear kept me under the table in the big room until Eaglebeak left – having promised to call again when my father would be home. With hanging head I emerged to face the music.

Instead of being angry my mother hugged me and begged to know what was wrong.

'There's nothing wrong, Mam. Honest. I'll pass the exam, you'll see.'

'But he thinks you're not concentrating on your schoolwork.' She was adjusting my tie and looking me straight in the eyes. 'Are you missing the old cottage?'

'No, Mam.'

'Are you being bullied at school?'

'No, Mam.'

'Is it some of the company you're keeping?'

'No, it's the company he's *not* keeping.' Gareth the Wise had just come back into the house after having made himself scarce when Eaglebeak arrived. I swore I would inflict terrible injuries on my brother if he dared say more. Fortunately he didn't continue; nor, mercifully, did Mam.

The film was thoroughly enjoyable, though surprisingly flawed. There was only one Welsh actor in the cast and the Irish-American accents of the others were completely out of place. One redeeming feature of the film was the hiding given to a sadistic schoolteacher by Dai Bando, the pugilist. The thrashing was cheered by schoolboys throughout the cinema, and I was shouting as loud as anyone until my brother took exception to my indecorous behaviour and ordered me to shut up.

That night Eaglebeak came to the house again and spoke to my father. I could tell that, despite the hostility which I supposed had existed between them in the past, they now appeared to respect each other. I tussled with thoughts about my judgement of people. How could this man who had hitherto so often epitomised the Devil incarnate now seem so saintly? Obviously I still had much to learn about character.

Dad and the headmaster concluded that my poor performance was due to tiredness; it was suggested that I start going to bed earlier – an idea I readily accepted. I also solemnly promised to concentrate properly and prepare myself for the big examination in the spring that would be so important to my future.

Life in the village proceeded in a curious, episodic way. Things happened like scenes in a play or a film, but for real. In fact some of the events, like Twm the Poacher's funeral, seemed larger than life.

Six of us sat on the cold rocks at the top of the steep field known as Cae Rhiw, from which we had a commanding view of the village. The ground in the shade of the trees behind us was still grey with frost which had arrived the night before and the sky was dark with snow-laden clouds. While we waited we tested each other's knowledge of the cinema, and it developed into a good-natured contest between the evacuees and the rest of us.

'No doubt about it,' said Peter Lawton, 'Lon Chaney is the toughest brute that ever was.'

'Nah, 'e's a cissy,' said Walter. 'Errol Flynn would 'ave 'im for breakfast.'

'Alright, what about James Cagney, then? Nobody *ever* beats James bloody Cagney,' said Martin Greaves.

Walter shook his head. 'Errol,' he said, 'would tie a piece of string around that dwarf's 'ead and use 'im as a bloody yo-yo.'

Albert Blenkinsop then played what seemed like a trump card. He dug Walter in the ribs and, rather in the manner of a toreador delivering the *coup de grace*, said, 'My Uncle Algernon works in films, see, and 'e's told me everythin' I need to know.'

'Wosseedoo, 'en?' said Walter, without flinching.

'Well, 'e works for Pathé, see, and you know the cockerel that's at the start of every newsreel . . . well, my uncle's the one whose job it is to grab its balls to make it crow!'

Right, Walter, I thought, cap that!

'All I can say is,' said Walter, 'it's a bloody good job yewer old uncle don't work for MGM!'

We all laughed like drains, before becoming aware of some movement at the top of the village about half a mile away.

The funeral procession had started at Twm's cottage and was slowly making its way down to the parish church. Our lofty vantage point gave us a perfect view of the route.

Juveniles were excused participation in this particular fare-well, for poor Twm didn't warrant the attendance of Scouts or Guides. And certainly no military presence this time. Twm represented an old, fast-disappearing native order of peasantry whose culture was of the earth, and it would be his fellows who would come to say goodbye. The 'Gentlemen Only' gathering of a hundred or more was strung out four abreast behind the horse-drawn hearse. As the mourners moved down the road their slowly- bobbing bowler hats were like ripples in a black river.

As the procession came nearer we could hear rumbling and the shuffling of feet behind the slowly-plodding black horse that led the way silently on hooves muffled with sacking. We could hear an occasional silicotic cough, but we couldn't see faces; and one bowler is very much like another.

The mourners moved down the narrowing road past the King's Arms, weaving their way around a stationary beer delivery-wagon before going temporarily out of sight behind a high thorn hedge that blocked our view of the road. The cortège re-emerged at the vicarage corner like moving lava, covering a large area outside the church gate before coming to a stop just as the snow started to fall. *Click, swoosh, floop!* With the precision born of much practice, umbrellas were opened and quickly raised to form an undulating roof. Within seconds the black canopy became speckled with snowflakes and was soon completely covered. The only unprotected heads were those of the six bearers who stepped forward to remove the coffin from the hearse. I recognised Wil the blacksmith among them and I wondered what was going through his mind, for he and Twm had been boys together. The hearse jerked a little as Twm's box was pulled out along brass rails and hoisted onto broad shoulders. A squeak from the vehicle's wheels was the only sound to break the silence until the crowd moved again and started funnelling through the little gate. An all-pervading whiteness made the scene appear a little unreal. Was it an illusion? Were they actual people down there? Was my old friend Twm really in that box? Even the stinging cold couldn't entirely convince me. At such times I could rely on Walter to put me right:

'Let's go down to the churchyard wall to say "So long" to the poacher.' He led the way down the slope and then, suddenly stopping, he turned to face us.

'Bare yewer 'eads!' he commanded. ''Aven't yew got no respect for the old bugger?' We doffed our caps. Walter himself had never owned one.

Now the bearers had entered the church with their burden. The mourners shook the snow from their umbrellas and followed them in until the church was full. We reckoned there were as many outside the church as there were inside.

'I'm frozen stiff,' said Martin Greaves. 'Can't I go 'ome now?'

'No yew bloody can't,' said Walter. 'Where's yewer respect for the old man?'

'Well, I never knew 'im,' pleaded Martin. ''E was just an old poacher, wasnee?'

'No, *not* just an old poacher,' asserted Walter. ''E was Geraint's friend, see.'

'Well,' I said, 'he used to cut my hair, that's true. And show me his pups. And he taught me about badgers and rabbits and foxes and pheasants and falcons and skylarks and wild flowers and all sorts of things. Yes, he *was* my friend, and I shall miss him.'

We could hear the organ playing the introduction to a funeral hymn, and then the congregation began to sing:

> '*O Iesu Mawr rho'th anian bur,*
> *I eiddil gwan mewn anial dir . . .*'

'O Great Jesus, fortify the weak in the wilderness . . .'

The crowd in the churchyard joined in the singing and the snow-covered umbrellas recalled a photograph I had once seen of an antarctic landscape that was like icing on a cake.

After a shivering half-an-hour that seemed a lot longer, I whispered in Walter's ear: 'Can't we let Martin go? He's frozen solid.'

My friend, who was nothing if not fair-minded, nodded. He went over to the snowman who was Martin Greaves and shook him vigorously. The boy's lips were blue.

'Yew two stay by 'ere,' said Walter, pointing to Handel Griffiths and me. 'Yew others give me an 'and with this 'un, and we'll get 'im 'ome.'

Blenkie took the feet, Peter Lawton and Malcolm Akister a shoulder each. As they carried him up the road, Walter was rubbing Martin's hands. I made a move to join them, but I could see Walter looking at me and shaking his head emphatically. I felt a lump in my throat as I saw him remove his own coat and put it around the lad's shoulders.

Handel said he hoped the 'vac' would be all right, but added that he wouldn't have missed my old friend's funeral for the world. He nudged me and nodded in the direction of the church's side door. To the strains of a dirge, the coffin was being brought out for interment.

At the graveside the vicar in his white surplice was almost invisible against the background. Despite the snow which was still falling heavily, every man furled his umbrella and removed his bowler. The many bald heads amongst the mourners came to resemble sugared almonds long before the vicar reached the committal. Then, at the appropriate moment, farm labourer and churchwarden Cadwgan Christopher raised a calloused brown hand and threw a fistful of earth into the grave. *'Lludw i'r lludw, pridd i'r pridd,'* 'Ashes to ashes, dust to dust,' intoned the Reverend Jones, going on to complete the ritual without a tremor in his voice, despite the teeth-chattering coldness of the air.

My feet were frozen and I knew that come the thawing there would be pain. However, that would be a small price to pay for the privilege of being there.

There was more singing. Amos Watkin pitched it for the closing hymn that included the words: *'O fryniau Caersalem ceir gweled, holl daith yr anialwch i gyd . . .'* the usual choice at a Welsh funeral: 'From Jerusalem's hills . . .'

The four-part harmony was uplifting but I could see many bowler hats held to the sides of faces to hide tears.

The hymn ended and Cadwgan discharged both barrels of Twm's favourite shotgun before tossing it into the grave. The sexton immediately started to fill the grave and bowlers went back onto heads.

'Da bô, Twm, hen gyfaill,' I said, my eyes full of tears as I turned homeward with Handel. 'Goodbye, Tom, old friend.'

I wondered about Greavesie, but Walter was looking after him, so I was sure he'd be all right.

A hot bath and warm, dry clothes awaited me at home, and, as the snow had stopped, I could hardly wait to get back out into the cold again. After all, a Saturday was a precious day and I wanted to make the most of it. The snowfall had given us a depth of about seven or eight inches and as it had come without wind it lay evenly. My feet had warmed up without as much pain as I'd expected and this time I took the precaution of wearing two pairs of wollen stockings. Gareth was boxing with Ronnie again over at Nant yr Arian and my father was still at work.

'Sometimes,' said my mother, with mock sadness, 'I regret not having a daughter. Men and boys are always out for some reason or other. A daughter would stay in and keep me company.'

'Do you want me to stay in with you, Mam?' I asked, confident of her answer.

'No,' said Mam with a smile. 'Of course not. Go on out. I know you can't wait!'

I began to think about Greavesie and went in search of Walter. The few pavements in the village had already been turned into long slides by the hobnailed boots of a score of boys. When I joined the gang some of them were taking it in turns to speed down the hill, but I couldn't see Walter. I ran about, ducking snowballs coming from all directions, and escaped by climbing over Bopa Angharad's hedge to the safety of her back garden.

I vaulted a perimeter fence and joined a lane to the rear of the dwellings where Walter lived. As a gate sprang shut I glimpsed a figure darting away from one of the back gardens. I couldn't swear that it was a man or beast, but whatever it was its furtiveness suggested that it hadn't been up to much good.

At first the screams and wails coming from Walter's back yard didn't mean very much, for his family was naturally noisy. But I really disturbed by the scene that greeted me. Walter's mother, who had the usual number of small offspring in tow, was sitting on an upturned bucket, hugging one of her daughters who was about nine years old. A boy of about five, the very image of Walter, was running around the garden sobbing bitterly. Walter's oldest sister, about fifteen years of age, was also crying but trying to take control, gently patting one sibling on the head and then another. She was the first to see me as I entered the yard.

'Oh, Geraint, where's Walter?' she said. 'We need 'im by 'ere now!'

'What's wrong Delyth? For God's sake, what's happened?' I said, trying to sound sympathetic, even though I didn't know what was amiss. Her answer was blunt and to the point.

'My little sister's pet rabbit's 'ad 'is throat cut an' 'e's dead.'

'Are you sure?' I asked, feeling a bit stupid.

'Yeah, 'e's dead, alright. *Very* dead.'

The nine-year-old started screaming again and I prayed for Walter to come quickly as I really had no idea what to do. As Delyth went to comfort her sister she saw that I was about to enter their shed.

'No, don't go into by there!' she shouted. 'Come away!'

There were traces of what looked like blood on the compacted snow near the shed door.

'Where's Mr Hopkins?' was the only thing I could think of saying as I backed away from the shed.

'My father's in work up at the quarry,' said Delyth. 'That's why I want Walter to be 'ere.'

'I'll find him, don't worry,' I said, my strongest instinct being to get away from the place. Cowardice can easily be disguised with a bit of bravado.

I found my friend at last. He was coming out of the house in Temperance Row where Martin Greaves was billeted with Mrs Roberts. Anticipating my question, Walter shouted to me.

''E's alright, mun! Warmed up now, but I thought 'e was goin' to pop it earlier on, aye! Went a lovely shade of purple, 'e did.'

As he came up to me he told me that Mrs Roberts had fussed over Martin and given them hot soup and a pile of Welshcakes which they polished off in front of the fire.

'I didn't want to bloody leave, mun, it was so good in there!'

I hated having to break the bad news to Walter, but I told him the story exactly as I'd heard it from his sister. I also told him of the shadowy figure I'd seen running away. Walter exploded.

'Dilwyn! Dilwyn!' he shouted. I'd never seen him so wild and excited.

I said: 'We can't be certain it was Dilwyn. I mean . . . all I saw was a shadow.'

'It was 'im, alright. I know it was.'

'What do you mean?' I said.

'Well, 'e stopped me on the road the other day an' talked to me all friendly, like. Asked me if I fancied some rabbit pie. Said 'e'd fix it soon. I took no notice of 'im cos I 'ad no idea what 'e was talkin about.'

Walter broke off to thump Mari Powell's wall with the sides of his fists. 'I should 'ave known 'e was plannin' somethin'! It's all my fault.'

It occurred to me that Walter hadn't sworn since I had told him of the tragedy. For once he seemed less than superhuman and I felt sorry for him.

'I'll go home with you,' I said, gently tugging him away from the wall.

'Nah, there's no need. I'll get back there now and sort everything out.' He struck the wall again and walked away. After a few paces, he stopped and turned.

'Geraint. Yew know I'll get 'im this time, don't yew. It might take a while, but I'll *do* 'im. Good and proper! I know yew'd want to 'elp, but this is for me to sort out on my own. Right, pal?'

'Right,' I said.

Chapter Seventeen

The snow quickly melted and as Christmas approached we were blessed with those special December days when the month seems to act out of character with lots of bright sunshine, though the air remained cool and crisp. After sunset it was cold enough to loosen teeth and no amount of extra clothing seemed able to prevent shivering. Still, we braved the night air to go carol-singing and were generously rewarded for the quality of our performance and admired for our healthy disregard for the biting cold. No carol was sung that didn't rise from the hum of Handel's tuning fork, tapped on window-sill, step, or door-knocker.

Bonfires weren't permitted during the blackout, but we managed to get away with hand warmers despite their bright orange glow. Holes were punched in the bottoms and lids of cocoa tins, old rags stuffed in and set alight. It was necessary to keep air passing through these devices, so we ran about like demented fireflies until the tins became too painful to hold.

In the week leading up to Christmas there were air-raid warnings on three consecutive nights. However, it was thought that the Luftwaffe had West Wales targets in mind for the aircraft were heading in the direction of Swansea, certainly to ruin Christmas for many folk down there.

The weather became milder and Christmas Eve was lovely – as if on loan from spring. Villagers walked with a sprightly gait as they visited each others' homes. They exchanged presents that were necessarily plain because of the shortages, but given nonetheless with conspicuous goodwill.

A cart had pulled up outside our house as we were finishing our breakfast. In a moment Uncle Gwilym was at the door with a piece of holly in his hat and a large cardboard box in his arms. Presents!

I swallowed the last piece of toast and leaped out to help my uncle into the house. Gareth, who was slowly drinking tea, glared at me.

'That's what's called indecent haste,' said my brother. 'Anyway, there's nothing for you in there,' he added with a wink at Uncle Gwilym.

After exchanging pleasantries with my mother and father Uncle Gwilym departed. He stopped at the door, looked sternly at Gareth and me in turn, and said: 'Not to be opened until tomorrow, mind!' Whatever presents the box contained were hidden by a layer of vegetables, eggs, cheese, and butter from the farm.

'Oh well,' said my mother, 'he'd have been hurt if we'd refused them.' Anyway, no need to feel guilty, for Mam would be sure to give most of it away. The other contents of the box would remain a mystery for another twenty-four hours.

But I had a lot less than twenty-four hours to do something I'd been putting off for weeks and which would require a degree of self-belief that so far had been in rather short supply. My first move was to go to the chest in my bedroom to remove a large 'Atlas of the World' from the big bottom drawer that contained all my private things. I thrilled as I lifted out a few articles which reminded me of birthdays and Christmases long gone: a conjuring outfit, jigsaw puzzles, sketch pads, and a cigar-box full of crayons. I then took out the atlas and opened it where Mongolia and China were depicted on one side with Siberia on the facing page. Between them I had secreted a neatly-folded piece of fancy blue paper I'd kept from the parcel from America months before. Then from the back of the drawer I retrieved the item I considered to be crucial to the fulfilment of my earthly destiny: the little bottle of jasmine scent.

On the pretext of going out to play I trotted from the house with the carefully-wrapped gift hidden in a pocket. I'd pinned to the little parcel a card which I had decorated after the fashion of those notes that Stanislav had dropped from the sky to his beloved Vera in an episode which now seemed almost a lifetime away.

I had set off in twilight, knowing that it would be dark before I arrived at Nant yr Arian. There was no clear plan in my mind as to how or where I would deposit the present; I just felt that this was my last chance.

I took the usual route up Maesglas and Lovers' Lane as far as the kissing gate, pausing there to rest and gather my thoughts. It was as silent and peaceful as ever. I assured myself that the benign atmosphere was due to the gate's associations and that fate had drawn me there; the fact that it was about the only route I could have taken anyway didn't occur to me, for I was being carried along on a wave of romantic optimism. And this time I was determined not to turn back.

The farmhouse was bathed in moonlight as I approached, and the sounds from the cowsheds told me that Ianto would be busy milking for a while yet. I knew that Ronnie wasn't at home because he had gone with Gareth to do some shopping in Cardiff and wouldn't be back until at least seven. Mrs Protheroe would most certainly be in the house with Annabel, so I prepared myself for a fifty-fifty chance of a doorstep meeting with the girl I had come to see.

Nervously I raised my hand to the doorknocker. There was still time to retreat. 'No,' I thought, 'I must go through with it. For my peace of mind. Once and for all.'

My hand touched the brass horse's-head knocker but failed to lift it. I sweated shamefully.

'My God, is it worth all this? I thought. 'Yes! Yes! *Yes!*' I told myself. I reached for the knocker again, lifted it, and brought it down hard, twice.

For the first time in months I felt free; there would be no stopping me now. I felt so good that I hardly noticed that my knock had set the dogs barking and they were now sounding off on the other side of the door. Someone else was there too, and I heard the sound of a bolt being drawn back. Who will it be? I thought, as an eternity went by. I gave a deep breath as the door opened and saw silhouetted against the light, the unmistakeable figure of . . . Mrs Protheroe.

'*A, bachan Ceinwen Llew efa? Beth wyt ti'n moyn?*' she said above the barking. 'Ceinwen's boy, yes? What do you want?'

I knew that my cringing days were over. I was polite but firm and answered in Welsh: 'Yes, I am Ceinwen's boy, Geraint. I've brought something for Annabel. And, if you please, I'd like to see her for a moment.' Remarkably, the dogs stopped barking.

'Of course, lovely boy,' said Mrs Protheroe. 'Of course you may see her. Come inside, will you?'

I followed her into the house and was guided through a door into the big living room that had a huge fireplace like Uncle Gwilym's at Caerwen. Annabel was kneeling at the foot of a tall Christmas tree that she was dressing with pieces of coloured paper, baubles, and tufts of cotton wool. She stood up and smiled at me without the slightest hint of embarrassment and I gave her a little bow! I could hardly believe what I'd done, but there it was – I'd actually *bowed*! That was the moment I realised that I'd seen too many films, but I could see that Mrs Protheroe was impressed. I hoped that Annabel was too!

'I've brought you a present,' I said, holding the package out at arm's length. She got up and smiled.

'For me?' she said, gently taking it.

'Yes, for you,' I said.

'Oh, thank you very much, Gerunt!' she said, and she walked over to the tree to place the package on the floor in front of it.

'How nice of your friend to bring you a gift,' said Mrs Protheroe. 'Do you have one for him?'

'Er, er . . . well . . . er . . .'

I rescued her: 'How's the tortoise?'

Her eyes lit up. 'He's hibernating,' she said.

'Of course, I should have known that. Well, I'd better be going.'

'See your friend to the door, Annabel,' called Mrs Protheroe on her way to the kitchen, and in a moment the girl who had been for so long unapproachable and unattainable stepped out into the night with me!

She seemed to glow in the silvery light and I was sure that the man in the moon was smiling. Here I was, with the most beautiful girl in the world, and I had her all to myself! I'd come to realise that I loved her totally. For her beauty, her poise, and her sweet nature. It was a good feeling, but somehow I still felt undeserving of her friendship.

Suddenly I was tongue-tied. Gary Cooper might have drawled a few words like 'Well, honey, I must be gett'n along now . . . things to do ya know.' Hardly my style!

And of course I didn't expect *her* to do a Hedy Lamarr, and say, 'Please stay, *please*, the night has just begun,' did I?

What she actually said was, 'Thank you again for my present, Gerunt.'

I looked into her eyes and said, 'Are you my girl, Annabel?'

'Yes, I *am* your girl. And you're my boy, aren't you?'

I could have cried with happiness, but I just said, 'Yes, *cariad.*'

'How do you say "Good night" in Welsh?' she said.

'*Nos da*,' I replied.

'*Nos da* . . . and thank you again,' she said.

Her eyes twinkled in the moonlight and in them I imagined I glimpsed our future. For a few more seconds we stood in silence. Then she turned and went back into the house, closing the door gently behind her.

I ran to the stone wall at the top of the field and cleared it easily.

On Christmas morning I got up early and eagerly opened my presents. They included a trio of books by Robert Louis Stevenson to add to *Treasure Island*, which I had read three times. Now I had *The Master of Ballantrae*, *Kidnapped*, and *The Black Arrow* as well! Inside each was a short note in Welsh from my father entreating me to keep broadening my knowledge by reading, but also to work hard at school.

The mystery of Uncle Gwilym's present to me ended joyfully when I unwrapped a small parcel tucked into the toe of my Christmas stocking. It contained a splendid pocket-knife with an inlaid mother-of-pearl handle, three blades, and every gadget I would ever need to hook, gouge, unscrew, and carve my way through the years ahead.

Gareth and I had combined our pocket money savings to buy gifts for our parents. My mother was delighted with a mock leather-covered edition of the Welsh Congregationalist Hymn Book which my brother had spotted on the second-hand stall in Cardiff Market. Dad was equally delighted with *The Essays of Francis Bacon* from the same place.

Just before dinner I heard a horse whinny and a few moments later Ronnie Webb was in the house, chatting with us. He said he would have to get back to Nant yr Arian quickly for Mrs Protheroe was already laying their table. Gareth and Ronnie exchanged small gift parcels and the latter handed me a package, saying it was from his sister. Even without looking at them I could sense my parents' curiosity.

When, through the front window I saw Ronnie flicking the reins and the Nant yr Arian cart rattling away, I turned fully prepared for the inquest. As it was, even my brother's gibe failed to provoke.

'Marry the girl,' said Gareth as he unwrapped his present.

All my normally loquacious father could say was: 'Well, well, well.' Before leaning over the table to lift the lid from the meat platter on which rested one of Jemima's plumpest chickens. He was carving it as my mother brought steaming vegetables to the table where my brother and I with hungry anticipation had taken our places. She then pre-empted any awkwardness I might have still felt and I silently thanked her for it.

'You didn't know it, but your father and I were sweethearts from the time we were nine years old,' she said, distributing the knives and forks. 'I'm glad you've got a nice girlfriend.' She then said grace, thanking God for our happiness and asking Him to comfort those who were suffering so badly in the war. During the meal my father reminisced with some anecdotes from the Christmases of his childhood.

Gareth had given Ronnie a woollen scarf and gloves; Ronnie had given him *The Pictorial History of Boxing* with which he was delighted.

Three pairs of eyes watched me me as I slowly opened Annabel's parcel. It was a book about London Zoo, containing many coloured pictures of exotic animals. Inside the cover was written: 'To Annabel on her tenth birthday with love from Mummy and Daddy.' Below that, in exemplary handwriting: 'My Best Book' and 'Given to my friend Gerunt!'

'Her best book!' I said to myself. 'She's given me her *best book*!'

'We'll have to make some more shelves soon, our house is beginning to look like a library,' said my father.

By New Year's Eve I had read *Kidnapped* and was half-way through *The Black Arrow*. Engrossed in the Wars of the Roses I didn't hear the noises outside the house. The sound of singing became louder, bringing my mother from her ironing in the back room. Dad, who had been dozing by the fire, woke with a snort and got up. Gareth returned me to the twentieth century. 'Come on, get up!' he said, 'It's the *Mari Lwyd*!'

The voices of the lead men Dai and Shoni could be heard above the rest.

'Dyma ni' n dowad, gyfeillion dinowad, i ofyn am gennad i ganu.'

'Well, here we come, harmless friends, to seek your permission to sing.'

My father and my brother went to the door to fight off the poetic challenge which was about to be issued by the visiting party, while Mam and I put the lights out, parted the curtains, and watched the proceedings through the window. The *Mari Lwyd* was a custom that went back to ancient Celtic times, but had since adopted some Christian overtones, hence the name: 'The Grey Mare' or 'Mary'.

'Mary' was a horse's skull topped with a white sheet and bedecked with coloured ribbons and bells. She had a hinged bottom jaw and if we'd dared to go outside, she would have snapped wildly at us. The custom called for the outside group to put posers to those on the inside, and, sung to a haunting ancient tune, the words of all involved had to observe a strict poetic form. Sometimes the contest would go on and on before one side would admit defeat. Should those on the inside finally be stumped for an answer they would be required to provide food and drink for the victors. However, it had become a local variation of the custom to call a truce after a certain time and the visitors were always brought inside. On this occasion it was a brief affair, for Dai and Shoni were no match for my father.

The exchanges went to and fro like a game of verbal chess for a short while, but I knew that Dad would manoeuve his opponents into a trap.

After about half a dozen verses in which Shoni had sung the praises of a prize boar, he sought to find a name worthy of the animal. Plausible titles were suggested from each side of the door, but all were dismissed as too mundane for the noble creature. The names being submitted grew in grandness until my father offered 'King George the Sixth' knowing that such an appellation would touch the sensitive nerves of the tradition-alist pair outside.

Thinking he could now deliver a winning line, Dai responded with:

'That would be offensive to our beloved ruler – an insult to our glorious King!'

It might have been more difficult for Dad to find a suitable rejoinder had Shoni not then entered the fray, to add:

'So we'll place upon our porcine paragon the greatest living Welshman's name: "Lloyd George".'

It was then that my father made the decisive move. In his ringing tenor he brought the match to an end:

'Such a name, my friends,' he sang, 'would be an insult to the pig!'

Checkmate! I saw *Mari*'s head droop as Dai, Shoni, and their helpers collapsed in laughter. It was all over.

Gareth opened the door and half-a-dozen men walked in. As they passed me I stroked *Mari*, who showed her appreciation by nipping my arm.

'She don't like losing, see!' said Shoni, with a wink. The little bells tinkled as *Mari* was placed on the floor by the dresser. How forlorn she looked now!

Mam, anticipating an early end to the good-natured dis-putation, had already laid a white tablecloth set with plates of bread and cake in readiness for the celebration. It was a measure of how much she had enjoyed the contest that she brought from the *cwtch* under the stairs the last earthenware jar of her three-year-old rhubarb wine.

It was an hour before the party moved off to try their luck down at the King's Arms; where, in defiance of the licensing laws, they would almost certainly see in the New Year.

I had no difficulty with my New Year's resolution. With new-found confidence I would develop my relationship with Annabel. This wouldn't conflict with my school-work, and in any case she wouldn't want the friendship of a dunce. I resolved to work hard and play hard.

During the long dark days of winter more thought would be given to local myths and legends than at any other time of year. Standing against Mari Powell's warm wall we'd contrive to terrify the more sensitive evacuees with chilling tales. Interestingly, our *Bwci Bo* was recognised by some of the 'vacs' as 'Bogey-man.' I had no idea how it pursued its victims at Chatham Docks or in the hop fields of Kent, but in Pengarth the awful creature was known to frequent dark corners of the village, ever ready to leap out from the shadows.

Naturally such talk led to the subject of Dilwyn, our very own Demon, and what to do about him. Walter wasn't with us at Mari Powell's wall, but the others knew what had happened and wondered what his latest plan for revenge would be.

'Heard about Walter's sister's rabbit, then?' said Mike Terenzi.

'Yeah, 'orrible, innit!' everyone agreed.

'Yes,' said Handel Griffiths, who claimed to know about such things. 'E's gone to 'eaven alright!'

''Utch, you mean. To the great 'utch in the sky 'e's gone, see, cos 'e *lived* in a 'utch, dinnee.' Perhaps Idwal had a sense of humour after all.

'If we 'ad any guts we'd do summink about that Dilwyn,' said Peter Lawton.

'Count me out,' said Mervyn Joseph. ''E's too big an' too vicious.' Murmurs indicated no enthusiasm for the formation of a posse that night at least, but each said he would go away and think about it.

*　　*　　*

Walter Hopkins left school in the middle of January and was taken on full-time by my Uncle Gwilym at Caerwen farm for a wage of fifteen shillings and sixpence per week. For Walter that was payment for being sent to paradise. 'I'm in clover, mun!' he said to me.

Without Walter around to direct us a few took up Mr Protheroe's invitation and formed a boxing club, meeting in the disused barn at Nant yr Arian where Gareth and Ronnie were already veterans.

On our visits for sparring sessions I would always knock on the farmhouse door to pay my respects to my beloved. Sometimes she would come outside until called in by Mrs Protheroe. I was always careful to keep my visits brief lest I should be deemed a nuisance. I would often say to Annabel: 'Please keep thinking about me, won't you!' To which she would reply in like terms. Then I would go and hit hell out of Peter Lawton or have hell knocked out of me by Blenkie, who was far stronger.

All the boxing took place under the expert supervision of Ianto Protheroe who, had he not been a farmer, would surely have been a manager or a promoter. He didn't have the enthusiasm for farming that fired my Uncle Gwilym, but his knowledge of boxing was very impressive. He turned us from plodders and flailers into flitters and dancers with rapid reflexes. He also taught us how to pull punches, for we were all friends and no one was to be really hurt.

When Ianto considered them ready Ronnie and Gareth were entered in the Cardiff and District Youth Amateur Boxing Tournament. The contests were held over five evenings at Cardiff's Drill Hall and were attended by a few dozen supporters from Pengarth who saw both our boys coast through the preliminaries. Ronnie was in a heavier grade than my brother so thankfully there was no risk of them having to fight each other.

Our evacuee reached the final and was matched against a boy who had been a Glamorgan Schools champion. When Ronnie was knocked down in the second round by a tremendous punch my stomach knotted. The Pengarth contingent groaned, and then roared as Ronnie, calling on all the advice he'd received from Ianto, got back up and dodged a shower of blows until the bell rang for the end of the round. The third and final round was a different matter altogether. Ronnie gave his opponent a boxing lesson and finally floored him with about thirty seconds of the round left. The lad got up on the count of eight, but it was really all over and Pengarth had a new champion.

In *his* final, Gareth's adversary was of a well-known Cardiff Docks boxing family. Hailed as a future British champion, Leroy Constantine had never lost a single contest since he had started boxing at the age of nine. He entered the ring with the self-assurance of one used to success; not as a braggart, but with quiet confidence. After hearing that they were to be the finalists my brother had spoken to him and was impressed with his sense of sportsmanship. In a way it was a pity that my brother had to ruin his dream. Gareth's strength was too much for Leroy and half-way through the second round the fight was stopped in Gareth's favour. Leroy's father and grandfather came over to the Pengarth camp with congratulations and high praise for Gareth. Afterwards, with the self-control of good sportsmen, neither Gareth nor Ronnie said much about their victories.

The success of the two Pengarth fighters led to a big increase in the popularity of boxing in the village and soon Ianto Protheroe's academy had several new recruits. On two evenings a week we had training sessions: skipping, sparring, and skipping again, until we were sharp enough to cut ourselves.

We would go home healthily tired after every session, but not before Mrs Protheroe, often accompanied by Annabel, had brought over plenty of bread and large basins of *cawl*. The broth would be ladled into soup dishes and we would eat ravenously in front of the big wood-burning stove that Ianto always kept stoked up in the old barn.

The pleasure we got from our boxing was second only to that obtained from rugby. From infancy our souls had become imbued with the spirit of that game. Ubiquitously exposed to the proud boasting of ageing men, the tinkling of medals, and the unremittingly watchful eyes that gazed from fading team photographs on cottage walls, we would remain forever in thrall to the mystique of rugby football. We would learn that the swell of pride in a victory quickly wanes, but also that the bitter pain of defeat is soothed by the essential camaraderie of the sport.

The war had brought an end to official games, but there were occasional matches between a fit and skilful side selected from Regular Army or Air Force units stationed in the area and a scrap Pengarth team of reluctant, older, balding men, conscripted *ad hoc* from the local Home Guard, Fire Service, and Observer Corps.

The games were notable for the high scores made by the visitors and for the conspicuous courage in defeat of our elderly heroes. On one occasion a youthful soldier was flying down the touchline with only Jabez Wilkins to beat. We shall never know how the old man managed to bring off the tackle of the century on the young sprinter. Some said he had been somehow able to regress himself to 1921; others maintained that if he hadn't heard his grandchildren shouting encouragement from the touchline he would have failed. Perhaps he would have been wiser had he just given the winger a little wave as he went past. However, Jabez hadn't survived trench warfare, a hazardous career working in the bowels of the earth, and a married life-time of nagging, to give up that easily. As the ball-carrier approached with the speed of a fox in full flight, a wheezing Jabez forgot his rheumatism and flung himself at him. The young soldier was brought crashing down and it was to his great credit that he was the first to go to the old hero's aid after the collision. The referee sensibly halted the game, while others rushed to help Jabez to his feet. I'm sure the old man would have carried on playing if he hadn't been driven from the field moments later by a very angry Mrs Wilkins, who had come onto the pitch menacingly wielding a sweeping-brush.

The hundred or so critical and fanatically 'one-eyed' spectators who turned up to watch makeshift matches were often treated to a curtain-raiser game between two boys' sides. I was both honoured and surprised to be selected as scrum-half for Pengarth 'Under Thirteens' in a match against Llantrisant.

The game was played at a hectic pace and at half-time honours were even, nine points each. As we stood in a group taking swigs in turn from a water bottle, I scanned the touch-line and spotted Annabel standing alongside her brother and Ianto Protheroe. I could hardly wait for the game to restart in order to impress her. I would perform magnificent jinking runs, side-steps, hand-offs, smooth passes, and save certain scores by grounding giant players with heroic tackles before an excited, wildly cheering crowd. I should have known it couldn't happen.

Rugby is a fickle game, with no place for the popinjay. All conceit evaporates with that first impact of muscle and bone.

My intended tackle on a charging wing forward was scornfully overwhelmed like a tank rolling over a dandelion. That was embarrassing enough, but as I painfully picked myself up, peeling the mud from my eyes and face, I saw Annabel looking at me and smiling. The rest of the match followed the same pattern: run, crash, tackle, pain, mud, smile. Annabel, Ronnie, and their guardian left before the end, which was a pity because although I was dismayed by the way my poor performance might have devalued Annabel's opinion of me, I wanted to show her how magnanimous I could be in defeat. It would be a long time before I learned that such considerations play no part in a woman's assessment of another human being.

My fitness and renewed zest for life had led me to hope that I'd seen the end of sickness. I hadn't been ill for many months, but February found me in bed with a temperature of a hundred-and-two and a wish to die.

'Influenza can be nasty. Be sure to keep the bairn warm.' In spite of the thumping in my head I recognised Dr Glennie's voice.

For several days I again suffered another acutely disordered state of mind. Everyone who spoke to me seemed incoherent. A series of hallucinations brought an interesting variety of visitors to my bedroom, including such diverse beings as Buster Keaton, John the Baptist, Bopa Angharad, Moses, Mr Smitherham, and Oliver Cromwell. Shirley Temple brought a message from Gary Cooper who said that he was sorry he couldn't come.

It was five days before my temperature dropped and the room stopped moving. The bedroom door was where it should have been for the first time in a week, and when it opened to admit my mother I knew it was she and not Charlie Chaplin.

'Visitor for you,' said my mother as Walter walked in and sat on a stool near the bed.

Walter was a tonic and I was soon laughing helplessly. He told me excitedly about the pigs, cows, fowls, and goats that he had looked after every day, but his most enjoyable job had been rounding up the ewes on the mountain. With Uncle Gwilym riding Princess Nest and himself on Owain Glyndŵr, he said he'd felt as if he was a ranch-hand in the Wild West, except that they were driving sheep instead of 'beeves'.

'I'm even getting' to like yewer Aunty Mari!' said Walter. I immediately sat up.

'Good God!' I said. 'What has Bopa Mari done to change your opinion, then?'

'Well, the poor woman can't do anythin' right, can she? Got to feel sorry for 'er, innit.'

'Why is that, then?'

'Well, she was doin' some dustin' this mornin' an' she had a nasty fall off a chair by the dresser and did some awful damage, see.'

'Did she break anything?'

'I'll say she bloody did! *Three* of 'em willow-pattern plates. Now it's a *twenty-one*-piece tea set! There was bits of china everybloodywhere!'

I was glad that Walter was swearing again and I hoped it meant that he was getting over the Dilwyn incident. However, his last words before he went left me in no doubt that he was still seeking vengeance.

'See yew soon, Ger,' he said, with a wave at the door. 'I'm goin' now to work out my plan to trap that bastard Dilwyn.'

After a few more days I had fully recovered and was allowed downstairs. Soon I was feeling sorry about missing school. This was offset to some extent by something quite unexpected – a visit from Ronnie and his sister. Their stay was brief, but important for two reasons. That Annabel still wanted to see me gave me a much needed boost. Secondly, the sheets of paper she left with me were to prove crucial to my prospects at school. In her truly beautiful hand she had written details of almost everything the class had been taught during my two weeks of absence!

After they'd gone my mother, arms up to her elbows in a tub of soap-suds, called from the kitchen: 'Your girlfriend is a remarkable young lady!'

Through some light drizzle, wrapped in an old raincoat and wearing a waterproof sou'wester, I went to the nearby woods and made for the biggest tree, a smooth-barked beech. I unclasped my new pocket knife and began carving. The outline of the first letter 'G' was taking shape nicely when I was over-come by a sudden chill; within minutes my hands became so numb I could hardly grip the knife. I abandoned the job and walked shivering to the edge of the wood where I paused to gather my thoughts. Something strange was happening and I felt confused. I realised that it had stopped raining and that everything about me was freezing fast.

Looking back at the woodland I was enthralled by a vision of sheer beauty: in just a few minutes every twig had been transfigured by a casing of ice. A field away, Pengarth looked like a fairyland village of glass, its telegraph wires hanging down like the cables of suspension bridges. Water that had been cascading gently from roofs had become glaciated; houses were draped with huge ice curtains, fluted at the hem and tasselled with icicles. I stood there awestruck, feeling that I'd perhaps witnessed a miracle; but there was more to come.

The first breath of a soft wind came up from the valley and instantly the forest responded. I listened in amazement to the sounds which were borne on the breeze. In a sudden miracle of transmutation tree branches became tinkling crystalline chandeliers. Fanned by the gentle wind they were rather like instruments tuning up. I could see no human movement from the village and I began to wonder how many might be missing such a glorious event. The woodland orchestra was now producing heavenly chords in a symphony that was probably beyond the creative ability of any mortal composer. The celestial music lasted for about five minutes before the wind gradually eased and the sublime sounds slowly faded away. As it became warmer the ice began to melt and eventually the whole experience was committed to the memory of the few, who, like myself, had been privileged to see and hear it.

Villagers tried to explain the strange phenomenon. However, my father's references to 'demise and renaissance' regarding the forces of nature were beyond anything I had learned either in school or chapel. And anyway I couldn't see the connection.

Reassuring my mother that I had been quite safe during the sudden freeze, I went to my bedroom and wrote an essay about the experience. The next day, to my joy, Miss Thomas liked it so much she made me read it out before the whole school. I was even more pleased to see that Annabel liked it, too. Some day soon, I thought, I must go back to the big beech tree . . .

*　　　*　　　*

Although the threat of invasion had long since subsided, the Home Guard continued to have training sessions. We sat on the high bank above a dingle at the Forlan fields and watched them being taught how to throw hand-grenades. What might have happened if they'd been using live bombs is open to conjecture. Some chaps were impressively skilful: not only could they hurl the missiles over great distances but they were accurate, too. Others, described by the instructor Mr Rogers as possessing 'distinct suicidal tendencies', seemed to have difficulty in achieving anything more than a short lob.

In respectful imitation of our proud citizen army we would practise our stone-hurling expertise in an adjoining field, always remembering to 'call the drill': 'PIN OUT . . . ARM BACK . . . THROWWWW!'

Chapter Eighteen

My newfound liking for school had changed me so profoundly that I felt a tinge of disappointment as the Easter holidays approached. My father with some help from Gareth had patiently guided me out of the numerical wilderness and I was at last beginning to get to grips with arithmetic. My work improved so much that I sat the big examination with confidence.

Some evenings I would repay my father by helping him rehearse his lines for plays to be staged by the Pengarth Amateur Dramatic Society. One was a comedy set in a large country house in Somerset, my father's part being that of a gardener wrongly accused of stealing the family's silver. My brother helped too and readings were often interrupted by our laughter at Dad's performance. He adopted a near-faultless rustic Somerset accent, no doubt deriving from years of friendship with Mr Smitherham. His memory of the lines was almost perfect and he rehearsed exhaustively. The old gardener would come in through the door doubled-up with arthritis, his eyes wandering around our room, recognising our meagre bric-a-brac as priceless ornaments; then with his tongue protruding from the corner of his mouth, he would walk around, guiltily fondling the pieces he particularly fancied. Occasionally he would reprove us for not keeping the action going. He would say, 'Come on, let me have the next cue . . . I can't stay in this position for ever!' And we would roll about.

The first performance at St Catwg's church hall was a near disaster. The play had a strange structure in which the second and third acts began in exactly the same way with regard to scene and dialogue. The cast were always aware of the risk of accidentally dropping the second act entirely if they should lose concentration; and almost inevitably on the night Gladys Jenkins, an otherwise convincing Lady Bolsover, did just that. Perhaps her first-night nerves were to blame, but she spoke the crucial line that was meant to take the third act plot forward. This effectively threw the rest of the cast, as Act Two had only just begun. My father came to the rescue with a piece of brilliant improvisation, putting the performance back on course with hardly anyone in the audience noticing the 'hiccup'.

Improvisation was evident elsewhere too. In a period when there were no new toys, gadgets, bikes, and other amusements associated with growing up, parents and fosterers had to leave their charges to their own devices. As the popularity of one craze after another rose and fell, some of my friends displayed spectacular inventiveness; not unexpectedly, the Terenzi twins led the field. Some of the contraptions they constructed from materials begged, borrowed, or mysteriously obtained, were masterly. Using lengths of wooden batten, strips of rubber cut from old tyre inner tubes, and sundry pieces of metal, they put together a catapult that could throw a cricket ball in the style of a bowler. By delicate adjustment it was even possible to vary the trajectory.

The same brothers introduced us to a contrivance which came to be known as the 'Terenzi Tank'. Comprising a cotton reel, a piece of candle, and an elastic band, the structure moved slowly along the ground for more than thirty yards. So many were made that sometimes the village pavements appeared to have been overrun by a plague of strange snails.

A cotton reel was also the key item in the craft we called 'cork work'. Mostly but not exclusively an exercise for girls, it involved criss-crossing and winding strands of wool around four small nails which had been hammered into one side of a reel. The knitted tubular shape which resulted from this emerged slowly from the hole at the reel's other end, and would be eventually sewn together to make scarves, table mats, and pot-warmers; also hats resembling tea-cosies for the less inhibited.

When we were not being creative we were being mischievous. Hardly a house was left un-rat-tat-gingered. There was, however, an unspoken and unbreakable code that guaranteed our respect for the bereaved, the sick, and the disabled. All others were possible targets for torment and we always selected those we considered to be the most deserving. But there were times when things went too far, such as the incident which came to be known as 'the case of the curate's eggs'.

About a score of us stood at the bottom of the Refail lane where we were joined by the Ingram brothers who came from the direction of Jemima's chicken run. In the pale moonlight we could just make out the bulges in their pockets and the smiles on their faces as they shinned up a drainpipe and spread-eagled themselves on the roof of the Reverend Raymond Vaughan's porch. I now realised what was intended, and although I didn't care much for the curate, he didn't deserve what happened to him. Eggs are fine when they are fried, boiled, or poached; less so when dropped onto the head of an unsuspecting cleric who was simply answering a knock on his door. Besides, in a time of shortages it's a shocking waste.

As I was missing Walter's company the holidays would give me a good opportunity to catch up with him. I decided to spend some time at Caerwen where he'd settled in well as an all-round worker for my uncle, and I left the house straight after breakfast on the first Monday of the holiday. Gareth had already gone to Nant yr Arian where he and Ronnie had arranged to help Ianto set up a new boxing ring. I could have gone with him, but I no longer felt the need to seek every opportunity to be near

Annabel; I believed that our relationship was sound enough and that she would not have wanted me to be too clingy.

The welcome signs of spring were everywhere and it felt good to be alive. In the village almost all the ever-early crocuses were out and about and many front gardens were already awash with the bold yellow of the daffodil. The fresh young greens of the hedgerows and verges were speckled with the softer yellows of the first celandines and primroses, and nowhere more so than on the sunny side of the grassy bank flanking the lane to Caerwen. Owain Glyndŵr grazed on *Cae'r Sguthan*, The Woodpigeon's Field, whose perimeter was immaculately hedged, apart from a section near the house where it gave way to some thirty yards of ranch-style fencing. Owain came trotting up as I neared the house, correctly anticipating the 'bit of something' I'd brought for him. The chunk of bread quickly disappeared; whereafter, understanding that 'that was it', the horse turned, gave a couple of frisky kicks, and trotted back to his sweet-clovered patch of field.

I knocked on the farmhouse door and went into the big room. Bopa Mari was sitting solemnly at the table and Uncle Gwilym was pouring a cup of tea for her. My aunt was dipping a flannel cloth into a bowl of cold water for application to her head. The scene was not unfamiliar, but I thought I'd better refer to it.

'Is there something wrong?' I asked gently in Welsh. Bopa just groaned.

'Pen tost,' said Uncle Gwilym. 'Headache. Your aunt is cursed with headaches.'

'Well, you can stay with Bopa then, Uncle. I'll take over. By the way, where's Walter working? Is he with the lambs?'

'No, he's not here at all as a matter of fact,' he said. 'I thought it was him when you came in. He asked me last night if he could come to work an hour late this morning and of course I agreed. He's two hours late now, though, and it's not like him to be a minute adrift. He's a good boy, that Walter.'

'What did he want an hour off for?' I asked quickly as an ominous thought struck me.

'Said he had something which had to be settled. I wonder what it was.'

'Sorry, Uncle,' I said, as I made for the door, 'I'll get back as quickly as I can. Hope you are better soon, Bopa.'

I ran down the lane and leapt over the fence at Cae Ton. Owain Glyndŵr lifted his head from the juicy clover to give me a brief glance as I passed. The short-cut across the bog at the bottom of the field would be the quickest route to the village and common sense told me I should try Walter's house first.

''E left 'ere at arpast six 'iss mornin' to go to work,' said Mrs Hopkins, putting one baby down to pick up another. 'I 'ope 'e's alright!'

'I'm sure he is, Mrs Hopkins,' I called back to her as I ran off, trying to think where to go next. I was feeling quite worried.

As I dashed through the village I thought of Walter's possible whereabouts and what might have happened to him. The facts were that he had left his home and failed to arrive at work, but only *I* knew the likely significance of his words to Uncle Gwilym.

My urgent questions to everyone I saw were fruitless; Walter was well-known, but he hadn't been seen that morning. I thought I might head for the mountain, but I changed my mind in favour of the Lesser Garth forest. Then Craig Gwilym ridge crossed my mind and even the disused air-shafts and bell-pits beyond Nant yr Arian. But then I thought: Dilwyn! If I was brave enough I would confront him and pull the truth out of him.

A surge of adrenalin sent me in the direction of the house where he lived with his mother and father, two quiet respectable people. Mr Price-Davies had a long-established connection with shipping. Their home was one of a group of large detached houses which had been built for business people just after the First World War. I'd been there once, delivering vegetables for Uncle Dai, and I'd been impressed by its size and elegance. I walked briskly up the long gravelled drive through a spacious garden that featured things of which 'ordinary folk' could only dream: a summer house, a sundial, and bird-baths borne by stone figures of discreetly robed Grecian women.

I looked to see if Dilwyn was lurking behind any of the pieces of garden furniture, trying at the same time to reconcile the loutish image with the conspicuously civilised scenario of his parents' garden. Well-satisfied with his absence, I walked up to the house and pressed the bell-push. The door opened to reveal Dilwyn's mother.

'Ah, come to see Dilly have you? That's nice! Afraid he's not here, though,' said Mrs Price-Davies. 'He's gone to that farm up on the hill; you know, the one . . . er . . . Ninety-something-or-other' they call it.'

'Nant yr Arian,' I said.

'Yes, dear child, that's the one. Said he'd be quite a while up there. Don't know why, I'm sure. Perhaps he's gone to join that nice little sports club they have there. Are you Dilly's friend?'

'Thank you very much, Mrs Price-Davies,' I said. 'You've been very helpful. Goodbye!' I turned and shot off down the drive, scattering gravel as I went.

I ran fast and wild through the village, up the church road, past Pegler's shop, and into the lower end of the Refail lane. The mention of Nant yr Arian had thrown me. What could Dilwyn's business possibly be there? The very thought of his presence near Annabel filled me with horror. I felt this was going to be a very important day in my life and that there was going to be a showdown. No Wayne, Cagney, or Cooper could help me now.

Dr Glennie's car was parked at the end of the lane and around it stood five men, one of whom was my father. They stood aside as the engine started and my heart skipped a beat as I watched the car race away. Dr Glennie didn't usually drive like that!

My father came towards me and put an arm around my shoulders. 'It's your friend the Hopkins boy' he said. 'He's been attacked.'

I felt sick. And frightened. 'Is he hurt badly?' I said.

'Leg broken, Oi think,' said Mr Smitherham. 'Oi found 'im lyin' 'ere as Oi was on moi way to the sharp. Wouldn't tell us 'ow it 'appened. 'E's in terrible pain, no doubt about it.'

I didn't speak, but as I ran off my father shouted back to me: 'Don't worry, he'll be all right. He's in good hands.'

At the kissing gate I paused for breath and tried to think of some strategy that would help me catch up with and possibly destroy Dilwyn. Fury alone wasn't enough, although I had it in plenty. I would have to face Dilwyn man to man – a sobering thought indeed! I needed a plan that would shorten the odds, as I was no match for him physically.

My heart was pounding as I gathered my breath and considered my options. If Mrs Price-Davies had been right about Nant yr Arian, her son shouldn't be far away. The boxing barn could be discounted, for despite what his mother had suggested, the bully wouldn't have dared to show his face in such a place. However, I felt in my bones that he was somewhere near and I moved up the pathway to the stone wall. The usual dull noises emanated from the barn, but it was another sound which took my attention. It came from near the copse beyond the farmhouse, an area still scarred by two-hundred-year-old

old bell-pits. Just like the iron-ore mines of the Lesser Garth, these old coal workings remained as ghostly reminders of generations of miners. Now I heard coarse, boisterous laughter together with something that sounded like sobbing. I felt that I had caught up with my quarry and must now close in for the kill.

I crept round the back of the farm's walled garden and into a small field before the copse. Then I froze, because about ten paces away at the edge of the tree line were Dilwyn and Annabel. I stepped out from the shadow of the wall.

'Dilwyn!' I said.

He turned, and I could now see what he held in his right hand. It was Lightning, the tortoise.

''Ello, Shortarse!' said the lout. 'We've been wonderin' where you were!'

I began to advance, and Dilwyn's left fist threatened me as his right arm began to move backwards.

'Now *this* is the proper way to throw a bloody 'and grenade,' he said. 'Pin out . . . arm back . . .' Annabel's scream pre-empted the final part of the deadly drill, and as Dilwyn paused I launched myself at him, driving my head hard into his midriff. He gasped and fell to the ground, whereupon Annabel scooped up the tortoise and ran to the house.

Mrs Price-Davies's darling Dilly slowly rose to his feet, breathing heavily and clutching his stomach. I stood with both fists raised in readiness for whatever would come next.

'Go to hell, you brute,' I said, fully expecting him to pounce on me with his superior strength and perhaps finish me off. I was certainly not prepared for what actually happened. Without another word Dilwyn turned and walked off into the wood.

I stood on the spot for a few moments, feeling somewhat drained but pleased with how things had worked out. Dilwyn, I thought, must be heading for home like the rat he was. My next move had to be to make sure that Annabel hadn't been too upset.

I was about to make my way to the farmhouse when I heard a sound from just inside the copse. A faint moan at first became the loud groaning of someone in intense pain. My God, I thought, Dilwyn's fallen into the bell-pit! I had grown up on so many warnings of the dire consequences of such an event that I felt quite horror-stricken. Bell-pits were about twenty feet in diameter and often covered with a thick tangle of thorny brambles and briars; accordingly, after reaching the wood, I proceeded very carefully, albeit locating Dilwyn wasn't difficult on account of the noise he was making.

'Help! Christ, help me!' I couldn't get a clear view into the pit but I could tell from his voice that it was quite a long way to the bottom.

'Sorry, Dilwyn, He's not here. Will anyone else do?' I said.

'Is it you, Ger? I'm in agony, mun! I need a doctor. I think my leg's broken.'

'Oh,' I said, 'First Christ, now a doctor. Does that mean you're getting better or worse?'

'*A doctor*!' shouted Dilwyn. 'Get me some bloody 'elp, mun! An' get me a doctor!'

'Sorry about your leg, Dilwyn,' I called down to him. 'But there's a problem. Dr Glennie's doing a locum in Ponty and Thomas the Vet's on holiday. And I don't know who else would want to help you anyway. You're not very popular in the village, Dilwyn.'

Dilwyn shrieked with pain and frustration. I'd have felt pity except for the thought of what he'd done to Walter and the business with the tortoise; and a host of other things besides . . .

I could have recited Dilwyn's life story to him. Not that he should have needed reminding that he was a repulsive bully and

a liar. Instead, I stood as near as I could to the edge of the pit and shouted: 'I wonder who'll get you first tonight, the rats or the weasels!' He was still shouting desperately when I left.

Swinging the heavy mallet, Ianto was driving in the last corner-post of the new boxing ring. Gareth was passing rope through holes already drilled in the other three logs and Ronnie was selecting lengths of tongue-and-groove boarding for the ring floor.

'No time to explain,' I blurted out. 'Dilwyn's down the bell-pit just inside the copse! He's maybe thirty feet down with a broken leg. You'll need some rope.'

Ianto immediately went for the block-and-tackle from behind the barn door. Gareth withdrew the new rope he'd threaded through the corner posts coiling it up as he went shooting out of the barn. Ronnie, too, hurried off, but not before I'd handed him the sickle that I'd spotted hanging from a nail in the barn wall. 'You'll need this,' I said. I genuinely hoped they would soon get Dilwyn safely out of the pit, but I wanted no more to do with it.

I wanted to see Annabel, but I thought that it might seem to be calling to receive praise for having saved her tortoise. I decided instead to go to see if Uncle Gwilym had any news about Walter.

At Caerwen they were better informed than I had expected. Uncle Gwilym had been to Pegler's and Mr Smitherham had told him of the discovery of the injured boy, who, it seems, had been taken by Dr Glennie to the Accident Unit at Cardiff Royal Infirmary. Although one of Walter's legs was broken, it was a simple fracture unlikely to result in future complications. He wouldn't work for some months but he'd make a full recovery. In the meantime, Uncle Gwilym would be allocated a 'unit' from the district Land Army – a couple of sturdy young women agricultural workers who would more than make up for the loss of Walter; albeit my friend's talent for comedy would be greatly missed.

It had turned out to be another busy day for Dr Glennie. Within minutes of returning from the hospital she had to go there again, this time with Dilwyn lying on the back seat of her car with his legs in temporary splints. My brother went with them at the doctor's request and he had some interesting things to say when he arrived back home at the end of the afternoon.

'We had a bit of trouble getting Dilwyn up from the pit,' he said. 'Ianto let Ronnie and me down by pulley and we put the lad carefully on the stretcher we'd made up from a bit of old canvas. He was howling with pain, saying he couldn't move his leg. He kept shouting he was sorry about Walter, and we didn't know what he meant. As a matter of fact it didn't all slot into place until just before the doctor and I left the hospital. Would you believe it? They're in adjacent beds! *Both* with their legs plastered up! Only Walter seems to be the happy one. Smiles a lot, so the nurses say. Seems he challenged Dilwyn face to face this morning and got the worst of it. He was thrown into the lane from the graveyard wall at Horeb.'

'I don't understand,' I said. 'Why should Walter be *smiling*, Gar?'

'Well, the irony of it I suppose. His attacker not only gets his come-uppance but has precisely the same injury. Only God could have written this one! And Walter'll be even more delighted when he finds out who was responsible for hospitalising Dilwyn.'

'Oh, and who was that, then?' I said.

'Come off it, Geraint! We know *all* about it. When the doctor dropped me off after coming back from the hospital, I called at Nant yr Arian. Annabel could hardly wait to tell me

216

how brave you'd been. Apparently she's told her brother about fifty times already.'

'But I *wasn't* brave. I was very angry. And a bit afraid, too.'

'It's usually enough, brother. Well done! By the way, you and I have been invited to Nant yr Arian for tea next Saturday.'

Gareth put on his Scout hat, took his staff from behind the door and trotted off to some gathering or other. I couldn't get what he'd said out of my mind. I did a Fred Astaire pirouette in front of the hall mirror before doing an Errol Flynn leap out onto the path. I ran happily about the fields for a while before returning home nearly exhausted; to a bath, a fry-up supper, and early bed for some more of *An Illustrated Guide to London Zoo*.

On the Tuesday Walter's father walked to Cardiff, returning with the news that both patients were in a 'satisfactory' condition. No-one knew if Dilwyn's parents had been to see their son. On Wednesday Doctor Glennie had business at the Infirmary and was kind enough to take me with her. I had no idea that the visit would prove so educational. In fact it was a milestone on the road to my understanding of human nature.

We entered through the big swing-doors and the defining smells of hospitals became stronger as we neared the wards. Threequarters of the place had been taken over by the military and uniformed personnel were everywhere. In spite of the notice 'Accident Ward, Authorised Personnel Only', I followed Dr Glennie to a long room with a line of beds along each wall. Most of the patients, all male, were heavily bandaged; several of them were sitting on chairs, while many of the bed-bound had plastered legs suspended from wire contraptions.

I gazed around the ward but could see neither Walter nor Dilwyn. The doctor spoke to a nurse who took us to a side room in which there were two beds. Doctor Glennie looked at the notes in the files at the foot of each bed and quickly read them. Walter spotted me first.

'*Geraint*!' he roared, and I feared for every sleeping patient in the hospital.

'Cor, this is a place, this is!' he said. Words poured from him in a torrent. 'Like a bloody prison camp, it is. Oh, sorry, Doctor, I mean a blinkin' prison camp, innit? Lights out at eight, wake yew up at six in the bloody – blinkin' – mornin'. Don't they, Dill?'

Was I hearing right? Was Walter actually speaking in friendly terms to Dilwyn in the next bed?

'Yes, Walter's right,' said Dilwyn. 'They wake you up for breakfast an' before you know it they're bathin' you an' stuffin' you with food again.'

I was surprised and bewildered to say the very least. I'd come fully prepared to ignore Dilwyn; but here they were, talking to each other like old pals. Doctor Glennie smiled and said she wanted to speak to the Sister. She left the room and I sat down on the chair near Walter's bed.

'How are you then, Walter?' I said, looking at his plastered leg.

'Oh, we're OK. Aren't we, Dill?'

Said Dilwyn, 'Yeah, we got two broken legs between us, see! Must be a soddin' record.'

'Yeah, but I didn't 'ave two good uns to bloody start with!' laughed Walter. 'Come to think of it, I might leave 'ere with two better ones!'

And so it went on. It was like a dream. But a good one, I began to feel.

Dr Glennie returned, looked at her watch and said, 'Geraint, it's time we were awa'.' Smiling, she patted both the plastered legs, ignoring Walter's 'I can't feel a thing, Doctor, not a blinkin' thing.'

'Goodbye, Walter,' I said. 'Goodbye, Dilwyn.' And we left the ward.

'It was good to see them friends with each other,' said the doctor as we drove home. 'And about time, too, I think. Don't you?' I had to admit that it was.

We reached the village and before getting out of the car I thanked the doctor for having taken me with her. She said that she would be happy to take me again and we said goodbye.

Without Walter I needed someone else with whom I could discuss the problems of growing up, their causes, and their cures. I particularly wanted to know whether it was right to hate as much as I did and whether vengeance was always a good thing. Gareth was as helpful as ever.

'You see, *brawd*,' said my brother one day as he sat on the low garden wall, as ever, polishing his shoes. 'No one is completely bad, or completely good.' Polishing hard, he said, 'There's usually a good reason for bad behaviour.'

'Yes, but it seems to me that some find it easier than others to be bad,' I said.

Gareth, pointing one of his shoes at me, said: 'Didn't you ever learn anything at Sunday School?'

'What do you mean?'

'Well, about such things as *edifeirwch, trugaredd, a maddeuant*.'

The Welsh words for repentance, mercy, and forgiveness always seemed to have enormous impact. I'd often heard them spoken from pulpits, and in such a way as to suggest the voice of God, Himself. Such words would leave a preacher's trembling lips as if blasted from a cannon and reverberate around the chapel. You would hear their echo for days afterwards as they resurfaced from the memory.

Satisfied at last with his shoes, Gareth slipped off the wall and went to the house, pausing in the doorway to say: 'The Gospel according to St John, Chapter Eight, Verse Seven. Read it again.'

In my room, I opened *Y Testament Newydd, Presented to Geraint Llewellyn for full attendance at Bronllwyn Independent Chapel Sunday School 1940* and turned to John's epistle. I began to understand why Doctor Glennie never questioned the deservedness of those whom she helped; why I, myself, had lost no time in seeking help on Dilwyn's behalf, and why Gareth, Ianto, and Ronnie had so readily hurried to Dilwyn's aid.

Not ready for sleep I went to the window and looked out into the night and wondered not for the first time about God. It seemed that there was no hint of repentance in the sound of the distant aero engines; no suggestion of mercy in the bomb-factories; no glimmer of forgiveness in the searchlight beams that would continue to pierce the night sky. Nor was there anything that encouraged me to think that life would ever be simply a matter of black and white; I already felt sure there would be a lot of grey, too.

Chapter Nineteen

Once more time seemed to slow down, and when I contemplated the Saturday tea that was still a couple of days away the clocks seemed to stop completely. Friday came at last and I was out of bed early. Gareth and I took turns to bath, don our Scout uniforms, and sit on a stool outside the back door for Mam to trim our hair. Since Twm the Poacher had gone, our mother had taken to barbering us, and although she was gentler with the clippers than the old man had been, her conversation often had a sharp edge. She took full advantage of our captivity to remind us of our current obligations and unkept promises. From first clip to last she catalogued the things we should do, should have done, and had better do.

'Don't forget you said you'd help your father in the garden this spring . . . *clip, clip* . . . tidy your bookshelves . . . *clip, clip*. . . gather some firewood for Bopa Betsi . . . *clip, clip* . . . help Mr Beer to white-lime the vestry walls . . . *clip, clip, clip* . . .'

Gareth got up, shook the towel that had been tucked around his neck during the ordeal and handed it to our mother. As he began the inevitable scratching inside his shirt collar he said: 'Yes, Mam, we'll do all those things, but first we've got a war to win!'

He dashed away as Mam deftly flicked him with the towel, stinging his ear as he passed. Then she sat me down and immediately began to recite the list of labours she had planned for her younger son. Although I frequently managed a polite 'Yes, Mam,' I took little interest until I thought I heard her say 'Nant yr Arian.' I was still rather receptive to any mention of that place as it was seldom out of my thoughts.

221

Finally, removing the towel, she looked straight into my eyes and said with a smile, 'So be on your best behaviour up there tomorrow. Be a gentleman, don't eat too much, and remember when to say "Thank you".'

'Yes, Mam.'

Saturday's prospects continued to preoccupy me, but the events proposed for Friday would certainly provide a temporary distraction. The village would be attacked on the ground by a mechanized army before midday and bombed from the sky after dark. Such mock raids were very serious affairs arranged to keep defence organisations on their toes, but they provided scintillating entertainment for those with a healthy sense of the ridiculous. Scouts would be 'injured persons' or 'messengers' – and mostly expected to stay out of the way.

Gareth and I joined the rest of our troop on the Groeslon, Mam having already passed our hats and uniforms as satisfactory. I took particular care over the positioning of the green stocking-tabs which she had ironed as carefully as if they had belonged to a Garter King of Arms. However, I couldn't compete with my brother's resplendence, for his tunic was arrayed with a dozen Activity badges, each one fully earned, proclaiming his reputation as the most versatile Boy Scout in the district.

George Rogers and my father were among the Home Guardsmen in charge and they sent Gareth and a few others to the branches of tall trees to spot the arrival of the invading force. On this occasion the attack would be led by a detachment of the regular army stationed at Whitchurch. Some of the soldiers had been with the British Expeditionary Force that came home via Dunkirk, so their imminent assault upon Pengarth would hold few fears for them! Nevertheless, neither they nor the numerous foreign personnel seconded to their units had allowed for the determination of the defenders.

The local defence force possessed no sophisticated communication gadgetry to aid them. Instead they relied on instinct and guile. My father lined up some Scouts who were good runners at intervals from the lookout posts in order to relay by the quickest possible means news of the invaders' approach.

We expected the attack before midday, but were shocked into action at half past nine. Luckily I was at the Home Guard control centre at Bopa Betsi's bakehouse when the first runner arrived breathless with the news that three Bren-gun carriers had been sighted making their way along Heol Goch, the road that comes up from Taff Valley. They would be in the village in minutes, so some quick thinking had to be done.

My father thanked Scout patrol leader Tony Thomas for his good run, and requested that he and three 'privates' follow him. I went with them to watch the action. Dad didn't seem to be perturbed about my presence, but I kept in the background anyway. When I saw them mount the steps to the bailey of Bopa Sarân's house at High Corner I guessed they were setting a trap for the military vehicles that were already entering the village. I found a good vantage point across the road from Bopa's, hiding amid the Japanese knotweed that covered the top of the high bank. From there I could see our men crouching in wait. I heard the rumble of little trucks long before they reached the Groeslon. They had been unchallenged up to that point, for the Home Guard men hiding along the roadside were under instructions from my father to let them pass.

From the expressions on the faces of the drivers and gunners when the vehicles came into view, it would seem that they were ready to claim an unopposed victory. If so, they were in for a shock. As the carriers turned down Temperance Road they were bombarded with clods of turf, deftly thrown by the men whom I guessed had been chosen by my father for their proven ability on the cricket field. There was total disorder as the three vehicles slewed and came to a stop, blocking the road. At that moment about twenty of the Citizen Army emerged from their hiding places and captured the nine enemy soldiers, who, with arms raised, were promptly marched away to the security of Wil the Blacksmith's big black shed. I slipped down the bank just in time to hear some bad news being broken to the large group of volunteers that had gathered to congratulate the ambushers.

'I'm afraid I'm going to have to leave you,' said my father, after he'd released the air from a few of the vehicles' tyres. 'I've just been told there's an emergency at the quarry. Somebody's had a nasty fall and they need me up there straight away.'

His departure was to be a crucial element in the day's proceedings, for it was clear from what he said before he left that his reasoning was sharper than that of his colleagues. 'Don't be fooled into thinking this battle's over,' he said as he handed his empty rifle to one of the men. 'Those carriers were decoys. They'll be sure to come in numbers soon and they'll be spread out. They'd have to be pretty dim to come up the main road. All you can hope to do is pick off as many as you can, one by one.'

He turned and left with a wave. It hadn't occurred to me before how much my father and Gary Cooper had in common! And he was right about the onslaught. At exactly eleven o'clock dozens of soldiers emerged from the forest and the copses, down the mountainside, along the lanes, and across the fields. How they had come so near to the village undetected was a credit to their training. Yet, despite their numerical advantage, they had difficulty in subduing the local militiamen who, although in disarray, were determined to fight to the last. As each prisoner was taken he was labelled with a sticky white tab, declared *hors de combat*, and directed to the Rest Centre, where he would receive a very nice non-belligerent cup of tea.

For the first hour-and-a-half the two sides seemed evenly matched, with the Home Guard using their local knowledge to pounce on unsuspecting soldiers from behind doorways, hedges, and fences, to claim their 'kills.' Gradually, however, the soldiers gained supremacy, and by midday there was not a single defender to be seen.

As if to rub the salt of defeat into the wounded pride of a beaten village, a seemingly endless convoy of lorries rolled up the hill and parked on every available patch of open ground. Before each one came to a halt soldiers were already spilling out, their boots clattering onto pavements and thudding onto grassy banks. Engineers quickly inflated the gun-carriers' tyres and swiftly unblocked the road. Twenty motor cycles with armed pillion riders snaked their way down Temperance Road and did a tour of Pengarth before joining the parked lorries at the War Memorial.

An open car began making a slow tour of the village, bringing more residents out of their houses, for in its rear stood an officer with a loud hailer.

'I-I would-would like-like to-to congratulate-tulate you-you the-the people-eople of-of Pengarth-garth.' The man's voice echoed its way down Temperance Road and normalised itself only when it reached the comparatively open space at Bron-llwyn. 'The marvellous resistance your brave army put up against a superior force was truly commendable. I have to warn you, though, that should the Hun ever honour this beautiful place with a visit, you will need to be ever stronger in your resolve. Today was a game. Some fine exercise for my men. Thank you, all.'

I made my way to the Memorial area and began to think of Walter. How he would have enjoyed the day's events! But soon I would experience something that would surely have made him leap into the air. The army was now at ease and a dozen or so soldiers were drawing tea from an urn perched on the back of one of the lorries. As I approached, I noted that not only was

225

their battledress somewhat different from the rest, but also that they were not speaking English.

I was joined by Gwyn Jones, the vicar's son, who began to chat to the men.

'*Bonjour*,' he said, with a sort of military salute.

'*Bonjour*,' replied a big man whose low-slung, Gary Cooper-style holster held a gun large enough to be a Colt 45. He poured what I could then see was coffee into an enamelled mug and came over to shake hands with us. '*Comment allez-vous?*' he said.

'*Très bien, merci*,' said Gwyn, delighted with this linguistic opportunity.

'*Ca va*,' said the soldier, '*Parlez-vous beaucoup de francais?*'

'*Un petit peu*,' said Gwyn. The soldier nodded and raised his eyebrows expressively.

'*Par example*,' said Gwyn, '*Je voudrais faire réserver une place dans le train partant à Paris à vingt-deux heures quinze.*'

'*Ma foi! Ca, c'est très bon!*' said the soldier, turning to smile at a few of his companions who had joined him, '*Alors, mon copain, continuez, s'il vous plaît*,' he said with an encouraging smile.

Gwyn shrugged his shoulders, and with his arms spread wide, palms upwards, gave a passable Gallic shrug, and said, '*A quelle heure part le dernier autobus? A quelle distance est le village le plus proche? Mais, sacré bleu! Au feu! Au feu! La maison, elle brûle! Et moi, j'ai une insolation. Domage, n'est-ce pas?*' Only later did I learn that he had asked for a train reservation, the distance to the nearest village, the time of the last bus, reported a house-fire, and complained pitiably of sunstroke.

By now every soldier was having a laughing-fit and the noise was drawing a small crowd of curious villagers of which Gwyn seemed quite oblivious.

'*Je ne peux pas dormir – j'ai une fièvre! Cela, ça n'est pas le rhume, c'est la GRIPPE! Et alors, je suis mal à la tête, et aussi à l'estomac. Hélas! J'ai beaucoup de peur. Aie! Aie!*'

The soldiers were gasping for breath long before Gwyn had so fluently apprised them of his fever, his influenza, his headache, his stomach-ache, and his fear.

Who knows how much longer he could have kept it up had not one of the soldiers composed himself enough to come over and say in (mostly) good English, '*Mon ami*, your French is very good indeed, but I'm thinking you may have swallowed a phrasebook, yes? We are Belgian, by the way.'

Belgians! Walter would certainly be told about that!

Half an hour later saw the last of the army vehicles leave the village at the end of an orderly convoy with the infantry following on. I stood on the Twyn mound until I could no longer hear the sound of engines and the crunch of boots. I walked slowly home to tea with a fairly clear head, thinking of nothing very much apart from Gwyn Jones's hilarious French, Walter, Dillwyn, Eaglebeak, Mam, Dad, Gareth, Ronnie, Gary Cooper, Rockfist Rogan, The Gospel according to St John, school examinations, the coming spring . . . and Annabel.

I was back in ordinary clothes for the evening's mock air raid. Others were in a variety of uniforms, from the sober dress of the Women's Voluntary Service to the strikingly bright attire of British Red Cross ladies.

The big stone slab in Bopa Betsi's bakehouse felt very cold. They laid me on it and I was glad when they'd finished bandaging my legs. Volunteers were fussing around and applying tourniquets and splints to healthy limbs. They also seemed to be applying iodine and other strong-smelling concoctions to any flesh that came near them. A young woman bound my head with a clean white bandage, which she then daubed with blotches of bright red ink. Proud of her handiwork she held up a mirror for me to confirm that the sight was sufficiently gruesome. After half an hour of such activity several dozen village residents had been given the appearance of a badly wounded host. There were those who considered it to be a waste of effort, iodine, and red ink. As we had already in reality been quite seriously attacked from the sky, they thought the time would have been better spent building sturdy shelters; however, they did concede that the exercise helped to nurture community spirit. For us, of course, it was fun.

My big day approached. It was fitting that the event decreed by fate to bring Annabel and myself closer together should take place on the sweetest of all days, a Saturday.

I awoke to strange muffled noises. I slipped out of bed and winced as the coldness of the linoleum assailed my warm feet. The sounds became louder as I removed the blackout sheet and drew the curtains. Two tractors had already started pulling potato-sowing drills across the field opposite and a few landgirls were laughing and chattering like jackdaws as they worked. Although it was no later than six o'clock, I was glad to be awake; after all, this was to be the Saturday of all Saturdays, probably the most important day of my life. Even so, I went back to bed to gather my thoughts, which by now were almost exclusively of Annabel.

The significance of being invited to tea hadn't escaped me. I knew that in our society it was a 'sounding out' device – a kind of personal vetting at close quarters. From listening to grown-ups I'd learnt that it was the stage which preceded 'getting one's feet under the table.'

Even though Nant yr Arian wasn't Annabel's permanent home, I could see the importance of obtaining approval from the Protheroes. There was no doubting that they liked me well enough, but this was different; I would have to say and do all the right things.

Gareth went early to the farm to help Ronnie put up their collection of sporting pictures on the boxing-barn walls. I gave him about five minutes start before following, as I wanted to be nearby in good time to settle myself. Wearing my best blue blazer, the new short grey trousers my mother had acquired through the Payments Club, and with a dazzlingly white handkerchief peeping from my top pocket, I felt like a real dandy. I was sure I could see the afternoon sun reflected in my meticulously polished shoes. There was a spring in my step as I went through the village and I was a bit disappointed that no one stopped me to ask where I was going. Clearly, to others this was just another Saturday.

A blackbird, very much 'on form', welcomed me into Maesglas Lane. Although so familiar, it seemed to me that the brilliant trills and changes had never sounded quite so beautiful. I have yet to hear the song of a nightingale, but surely for a matinee performance few birds if any can upstage a cock blackbird if it's in the right mood.

As I crossed the big meadow the scattering rabbits seemed to know that this was *my* day, pausing as if to say Cheerio before disappearing. When the kissing gate came into view I slowed down and pondered what to do next. I was an hour early and the last thing I wanted to do was join Gareth and Ronnie at the barn as that would have distracted me.

I stood inside the gate breathing the spring air fragrant with fresh, herby aromas from the hedgerows. Chaffinches chinked, and in nearby hazels the acrobatics of a pair of great tits caused catkins to dance daintily like tiny puppets. Tortoiseshell butterflies flitted about young nettles and thistles. Only a few weeks earlier the woebegone hedges and banks had looked pretty wretched; now, drabness had given way to an eruption of colourful life, an exuberant celebration that perfectly fitted my mood.

I became aware of an aroma, at first scarcely noticeable, but steadily increasing in intensity. It was tantalisingly familiar, but I just couldn't identify it.

'Hello, Gerunt,' said Annabel.

She was standing about five paces behind me and the subtly powerful waves of perfume pleasured my nostrils as I turned to face her.

'Annabel!' I said. 'Jasmine!'

She frowned. 'Oh, I expect I put too much on. But it really is nice. It was very kind of you. And now I can thank you for something else.'

'Oh,' I said, 'And what would that be?'

'For rescuing me from that Dilwyn and for saving Lightning.'

I felt about ten feet tall, but I managed a smile and said that it was nothing.

'Oh *no*,' she said, 'it *was* something – and a very brave something too.'

We moved a few steps away from the gate, sat down with about a yard of grassy bank between us, and looked at each other.

'You've got green eyes,' she said.

'That's funny,' I said, 'I don't feel a bit jealous at the moment.'

She laughed. 'They're *blue*-green really.'

'I like yours, too. They're blue – like Betty Grable's.'

'Who's Betty Grables?' she said, with the merest hint of a frown.

'Betty *Grable*,' I said. 'She's a film actress and very beautiful.'

'Oh, that's all right, then,' said my lovely girl. 'Now let's talk about other things.'

'Like what?' I said.

'Well, like what does "Nanteeryan" mean?'

'It means a silver brook or stream,' I said. *Nant yr Arian* – a *nice* name don't you think?'

'Yes, it is. Say some more Welsh, Gerunt. Tell me a Welsh story.'

I moved a little closer to her and for a moment I felt speechless and almost overwhelmed by a radiance that seemed to match the sunshine of that beautiful spring day. The air was so potently laced with the scent of jasmine that I felt almost intoxicated.

Annabel's floral-print cotton dress had been crisply ironed. Her white socks contrasted nicely with her blue summer shoes. Her golden hair fell loosely about her shoulders and her sweet face fascinated me. Why did she have this effect on me? Why should a movement of her head or the slightest frown move me so much? Why did I feel that, if necessary, I would be ready to die for her? I wondered if indeed we could have met in another lifetime. I took a deep breath.

'All right, then, a Welsh story,' I said, knowing that from the many well-remembered legends there was only one that seemed to perfectly fit the occasion; for Annabel was so evocative of one of the most beautiful characters in our immensely rich folklore. My girl, I thought, must be told of the lovely Olwen – the jewel of the *Mabinogion*.

'Olwen,' I whispered to myself.

'Who?' said Annabel.

'Olwen,' I said, seeming to recognize in her the legendary beauty.

Again moving a little closer to his listener, Geraint the Storyteller began his tale:

'Once there lived a handsome youth whose beautiful, dappled-grey horse had a saddle and a bridle of priceless shining gold. His name was Culhwch.'

'Keelhook?'

'Yes,' I said. 'That'll do.'

'He'd been sent by his father to the court of Arthur to find a beautiful maiden who was the daughter of a giant. As he rode he held in one hand two silver spears with edges sharp enough to wound the wind. At his hip was a golden sword inlaid with a cross as bright as lightning. With him were two white hounds with ruby-studded collars. They darted around the horse and its princely rider like graceful swallows. Culhwch's shoulders were draped in a cloth of purple that bore a golden apple at each corner.'

'Mm! That's lovely,' said Annabel.

'He was told by the great Arthur where the beautiful Olwen could be found, but a year went by and Culhwch had still not found the creature of his dreams.'

'Oh dear,' frowned Annabel.

'So Culhwch set out with a band of Arthur's chivalrous knights, including Kai of the wondrous skills and others of magical powers. At last a strange-looking castle appeared in the distance, but though they spurred their chargers onward the castle came no nearer.'

I speeded up a little to tell of some of the adventures and casting of spells that took place before Culhwch saw the exquisite maiden for the first time; but I 'laid it on' a bit, too:

'She was clad in a robe of flame-coloured silk and about her neck sparkled precious emeralds. Her hair was the yellow of broom, her skin whiter than the sea-foam, her hands fairer than blossoms of the wood anemone.'

Annabel's eyes were shining as I continued:

'Her eyes were bright as a falcon's, her cheeks were rose-pink, her bosom as white as swansdown. Culhwch was so stricken by her beauty that for a while he could only stare in wonderment. As Olwen moved towards him the young knight was astonished to see that from wherever her feet had trodden there sprang up four trefoils, white and bright against the green grass. Culhwch felt he had died and gone to heaven!'

While I had been speaking Annabel had moved closer to me. Now she took my hands in hers and we both got up. We didn't speak as she gently led the way back to the kissing gate. We reached it as, from the top of a nearby hawthorn, the local blackbird as if 'on cue' melodiously welcomed us.

'We've got a blackbird at home,' said Annabel. 'But he doesn't sing like that! Lovely, isn't it ?'

'Yours is probably a young bird,' I said, 'and he'll probably get better as he gets older. They learn, you see. In any case this is an enchanted spot. Blackie there is probably an old Celtic spirit in the form of a bird.'

'Do you really believe that?' said Annabel, wide-eyed in wonderment.

'Why not?' I said.

'I'll think about that,' said Annabel. 'But it *is* a lovely place, Gerunt. We'll come here often, won't we?'

'Yes, we will,' I said. 'We'll have picnics. Over there by the ash tree.'

'Lovely!' said Annabel.

With a gentle hand on each of her shoulders, I looked into the beautiful blue eyes and said, 'I will love you for ever, Annabel.'

'I will love *you* for ever, too,' she said. 'You are my Keelhook and I am your Olwen, aren't I?'

'Yes,' I said, 'You are. You always were. Always will be.'

Leaning close to her I kissed her on the cheek; and then, a mite nervously, on her lips.

That second kiss remains indescribable. But its lasting effect upon me was that of a sea-change. I may not have been fully aware of it, but I was putting behind me my callow childhood with its headful of dreams and fanciful notions. A lifetime of discovery and new perspectives was just beginning.

Silently, but delightedly, we embraced . . . until a loud call replaced the song of the blackbird – who'd probably decided to call it a day anyway.

'AAAAAAANNABEL!'

'My God,' I cried. 'It's Tarzan! What's *he* doing in Pengarth? He's supposed to be in Africa!'

'It's not Tarzan,' said Annabel. 'It's Mrs Protheroe, and it's tea-time.'

'What about Olwen?' I said. 'I was only half-way through the story.'

Annabel smiled.

'Right,' I said, 'let's go.'

Ronnie and Gareth were already in the house washing their hands. Mr Protheroe was hovering about, shadow boxing, demonstrating subtle swerves and other defensive stratagems. Upon seeing me he threw a straight left which he cleverly stopped an inch from where my nose would have been; but I had instinctively dodged and countered with a blow to his midriff, which stung my fist as it connected with his watch-chain.

'*Da iawn, 'machan i,*' he said, laughing and tapping me on the head. 'Very good, my lad. That's exactly what I've been teaching this pair.'

He entered the big room where the tea was laid and, seeing Annabel, said, 'This boy will look after you for ever, no doubt about it!'

He was obviously referring to what he saw as my promising pugilistic skills, but that wouldn't have occurred to the girl.

'Yes, Mr P., he's my gallant knight.'

Mrs Protheroe directed us to our chairs, and after saying a Welsh grace she besought us to 'clear the lot' – a crude but well-meant entreaty that was going to be difficult to honour in view

234

of the mountain of food before us. I was placed opposite Annabel and Gareth faced Ronnie. Mr Protheroe sat at one end of the table and his wife at the other, from which she had easy access to the kitchen. Between sandwiches and cakes that had little of a wartime look about them we chatted vigorously. For the first time I learned of the Webb family and their home, and I felt a twinge of guilt for never having taken the trouble to find out about these things.

The information gap was filled by Ronnie, who talked breathlessly about their parents. We were told that their father was named Matthew, after the channel swimmer of the previous century. Hearing that their mother's name was 'Helen', my mind flashed back to the naming of the poor creature from which we'd stolen the silk all those months ago. Annabel must have been thinking of her faraway mother more than I had realised.

'Dad works at Chatham Docks,' said Annabel's brother proudly. 'He's a foreman stevedore. Was in the navy as a boy. Can carve ships in bottles. Good swimmer. Good cricketer too. Had a trial for Kent. Used to take us hop-picking and fishing. Likes growing roses. He goes to the pub every Friday and he promised he'd get us a bike each one day. He loves repairing clocks because that's what he used to do to while away the time at sea when he wasn't making ships in bottles or doing water colours of birds and porpoises and dolphins. Sent us a letter last week and asked if we were all right, and had we made many friends, and not to worry – the war won't last for ever and don't worry about Mum either. She's OK and sends her love. And please let her know if Lightning's all right . . .'

At this point the farmer leaned across and put his arm around Ronnie's shoulders and said: 'Yes, it must be hard for you to be away from home and your parents, but if you can stick it out you'll be all right here with us.'

'Yes, I know that, Mr P. Thank you,' said Ronnie, his bottom lip quivering slightly. I looked across at Annabel and although she smiled at me I could see she had been affected by Ronnie's nostalgia.

'Right!' said the farmer's wife, slapping her thighs and getting up, as though to change the conversation. 'How about a nice cup of tea?' I wondered how many times that simple phrase had earned its keep!

Mr Protheroe brought out an old atlas for Ronnie to show him where Chatham stood on the Medway estuary. Annabel spoke brightly but not mawkishly about her home and the collection of dolls she kept in a glass-fronted cupboard that her father had made for her. Her words were directed at her guardian, but I had no doubt that they were partly for my benefit. We learned that her mother was a beautiful woman who, as a young girl, had worked as a maid in a smart London household, but had not liked it. On leaving that employment she had received two parting gifts: her train fare home to Chatham and a young unwanted tortoise.

By the time we were fully jellied and blancmanged I felt like a boa constrictor that had just swallowed a goat.

As we were leaving Mrs Protheroe gave me an impressively handsome present. In English, and clearly for Annabel's ears as well as mine, she said, 'Don't forget now, Geraint Llewellyn, you are welcome to come here any time to see this young lady.'

My feet were well and truly under the table!

Chapter Twenty

Within a week I was again reminded of life's snakes and ladders. There had been a lull in the bombing of south-east England and the authorities were encouraging evacuees to return home for short stays, an idea which met with the approval of children and parents alike. Annabel must have been just as homesick as her brother and on that day at Nant yr Arian she had put on a brave face for my benefit.

Their departure happened too quickly for me even to wish them a safe journey, but in a couple of days I received an envelope addressed in an unmistakeable hand:

Dear Gerunt,

Sorry I couldn't say goodbye to you when we went off. The bus came at 8 in the morning. I was crying when we left but I'm alright now. Mum was pleesed to see us and Lightning. I don't know if Lightning was pleesed to be back because it's hard to tell how a little tortoyse feels. I went to the park today and guess what I saw. It was a kissing gate the only one left in Chatham. All the other gates and rilings have been taken out for melting down for the war. I kept dreaming about us at the gate, it was just like the pichures. Oh I never told you who my favorit film star is. Well its Garrie Cooper. Have you ever seen him? He's the best! I still love you and I know you still love me. You said it was for ever. That means we'll be married one day and have lots of children and granchildren wont we. I wonder what you'll be by then a judge I expect or a film star or King of Wayles? I'll be back soon and then we can pick names for our children. Ones I can say properly. I expect you will go to the gate and think of me.

For ever and ever
Annabel

I tucked the letter into the inside pocket of my jacket and several times removed it to read again. I would have to reply to it as soon as possible, but with carefully chosen words; after all, Annabel would be my future partner in life. But the job would have to wait a while as a visit to Walter was overdue.

*　　*　　*

Gareth and I walked the three miles down the valley to catch the train to Cardiff. The smells and sounds of a railway station had always fascinated me for they were not of my upbringing; the approaches to Pengarth were too steep for a railway. On the station platform at Taff's Well, a chocolate-dispensing machine stood as a reminder of the days when, by inserting a silver threepenny-bit, you could draw from that magical iron box a bar of Fry's dark chocolate with a minty cream filling. On the outer wall of the booking office large enamelled signs now made redundant by the war, but still advertising Ovaltine, Bisto, and other delights, were starting to rust at the edges. We walked up and down with Gareth issuing brotherly warnings about going too close to the platform's edge. Fifty yards away a signal clunked as it fell, and soon a short hoot heralded the arrival of the two o'clock train. Forty-five minutes later we were walking into Walter's ward at Cardiff Royal Infirmary.

Our first shock was finding that the beds in which I had previously seen Walter and Dilwyn were empty. A knock on the door marked 'Sister McCarthy' brought out a stout, stern-looking woman in dark blue, whose eyes brightened at the mention of Walter's name.

'Well, now,' she said, 'your guess is as good as mine as to where *he* might be. He's the life and soul around here, bless him. He's already up and about on crutches and he's so helpful we let him go almost anywhere. I think the dear boy was sent by the good Lord to entertain us!'

Loud laughter drew us to a little kitchen where Walter, with his back towards us, was propping himself up on one crutch and pouring tea into cups placed on a trolley bound for the ward. Two nurses were watching him and shaking with laughter.

'Oh, stop it, will yer!' said the one with the red hair, flopping onto a stool with her hands over her stomach. 'We'll be havin' Matron down here, for sure!'

But her colleague recognised us as rescuers. 'Is it comin' to take 'im away, y'are?' she gasped. 'Oi really don't t'ink we can take anny more!'

Walter turned to face his visitors and whooped like a war-happy Comanche. After we'd hugged each other he introduced us to Kathleen and Nuala, who, like many of the nursing staff, were from the Emerald Isle. Walter had been 'comparing notes' regarding living standards in our respective countries.

'What've you been telling them, Walter?' said Gareth.

Before Walter could reply, Kathleen said, 'Well, Oi'll tell yer somethin' now. We've been t'inking our poverty back home was bad enough, but it can't be anyt'ing like yours, that's for sure. I mean, like . . . well, Walter, here, says 'is family's so poor that they've gotta borrow next door's meat to make gravy!'

'That's the gospel trewth!' protested Walter. 'Tell that to *most* people an' they'd never believe yew!'

The girls were still laughing after we'd said goodbye, to follow Walter slowly down the corridor to the Visitors Room.

Walter's recovery had surprised his doctors. His leg was still plastered but fortunately he was able to place one foot on the floor to steady himself between the propelling crutches. We reached the Visitors' Room, found ourselves a suitable corner, and sat down.

'Go on, 'en,' said Walter, 'Ask me the question. Gerrit it off yewer chests!'

Gareth and I looked at each other and my brother said: 'Don't know what you mean, Walt. What question?'

'Like "Where's Dilwyn?" That'll bloody do. "Where's Dilwyn?" Didn't yew miss 'im when yew came in?'

'Yes,' said Gareth, 'but we assumed he was in the lav or something.'

'No, mun,' said Walter, leaning closer to us and lowering his voice. 'They've moved 'im to a *special* 'ospital. One with a big wall round it!'

'You don't mean . . . ' I began.

'Yeah, I do bloody mean,' said Walter. 'The men in white coats came yesterday an took 'im away to Bridgend. See, when I was 'ere in the next bed to 'im I was told by the doctors that 'e was daft but 'armless. They asked me to be friendly to 'im, like, and that's why it looked like we was big mates when yew came in that time, see.' He looked at his feet and frowned.

'Good God!' I said. 'That explains it, then. You certainly fooled *me*. Oh dear. Poor Dilwyn.'

'Yeah,' said Walter. 'Poor sod. You know, I'd almost got to like 'im.'

'But what did he *do*, Walter?' said Gareth, 'Why did they have to take him to Bridgend?'

'Well,' said Walter, 'they 'ad to send for 'is parents, cos 'e'd been caught pourin' medicines down the sink, see. 'E'd raided a cupboard when no-one was lookin'. See, 'e *could* get about a bit, although 'e was still in a wheelchair. Anyway, then 'e threatened one of the doctors with a table knife. That was after 'e'd said that given 'alf a chance 'e'd strangle the ward Sister. And the Matron too, innit? Well, 'e was obviously off 'is rocker, wasnee? Anyway, 'e got to be shoutin' an' swearin'. Really bad, like. But I reckon it was 'is *threatnin'* everybody that *really* did it. So now 'e's *certified* – well, that's the word they used, like.'

Walter paused, and then said: 'P'raps they *can* do somethin' for 'im. I 'ope so, anyway.'

'*Poor, poor* boy,' said Gareth. 'We have to feel sorry for him. He must be in torment.'

'I'll tell yew what,' said Walter, looking as solemn as I'd ever seen him, 'I cried myself, too, when I saw 'is mother and 'is father sobbin' by 'ere yesterday.'

We changed the subject and updated Walter with gossip from the village. Eventually the matter of the last mock raid came up and I remembered that I wanted to tell him about the foreign soldiers.

'Believe it or not, they were Belgians!' I said, and his response surprised me.

'P'raps one or two of 'em were my relatives,' he said.

'What do you mean?' I said, and felt a little kick on my shin from Gareth.

'Well, I thought yew knew,' said Walter. 'My grandfather left us when I was about three. 'E went back to Belgium where e'd been in the Great War, see. 'E'd been friendly with a young woman there in 1918. 'E never came back and my family never did forgive the old clown.'

At last, the mystery solved! 'So you've got nothing against the Belgians, then?' I said.

'No, 'course I bloody 'aven't! Anyway, never mind my old Grampa's romancin', 'ow's yewers gettin' on?'

Caught on the hop, I had no immediate answer, but Gareth did the necessary:

'Feet under the table, believe it or not,' he said. *'Feet under the table!'*

'Oh,' said Walter, giving me an old-fashioned look. 'Like *that*, is it?'

I gave him a big smile and said nothing.

After proper and sincere expressions of sympathy and best wishes for a rapid return to full health and strength, we left Walter to the exemplary care for which Cardiff's Royal Infirmary had become rightly famous. His last words to us were typical of the very special person I knew him to be. I can still see him standing at the top of a staircase, a crutch firmly clasped in each armpit:

'See, boys,' he called after us. 'As yew slide down the bannister of life, yew'll always find a few splinters pointing the wrong bloody way!'

Walter always had a way of making an old joke sound fresh.

*   *   *

Other 'vacs' had also gone back home for short stays, and they were greatly missed, both in and out of school. The impression they had left on our village was stronger than we had imagined and their sudden departure had moistened many eyes. Tears were shed for Dilwyn, too, because being 'taken to Bridgend' was the equivalent of being 'sent to the Front' – a place from which persons often didn't return. Despite the undoubted normality of (most of) its inhabitants, the name of the town had unfortunately become associated with the irredeemably mad. However, sincere pity was always felt for the sufferers and their families. Hence: 'Oh, that *poor* boy!' and 'Those *poor* Price-Davieses!'

My mother was stirring clothes in the bubbling water of a cauldron on top of our electric cooker. I could hear her saying to herself '. . . *druan bach . . . pûr dab . . .*', 'poor boy, poor boy.'

I was sitting at the kitchen table waiting for some inspiration for my letter to Annabel and being somewhat put off by the strong smell of 'Sunlight' soap.

'What are you writing?' asked Mam, pointing at my blank writing pad with her wooden dolly.

'Nothing, so far,' I said. It wouldn't have mattered if Mam had pressed me further, for I had now overcome the embarrassment of having a girlfriend. However, at that moment 'The News' came on the wireless and my mother turned up the volume. There were reports of the continuing blitz over London, but also ominous descriptions of the movements of German and Italian ground forces in North Africa. *Libya . . . Benghazi . . . Tripoli . . . the Afrika Korps . . . Rommel . . .*

Every now and again I could see Mam shaking her head.

The last news item conveyed the warning that the almost inevitable introduction of clothes rationing was just around the corner. My mother's comments indicated that her reaction to this announcement would have been dramatically demonstrated had Adolf Hitler entered our kitchen at that moment.

George Formby's guest performance during the 'Workers' Playtime' broadcast that followed made me determined to start ukelele lessons as soon as possible; it also made me realise that serious letter-writing in the kitchen at that time was out of the question. I pocketed my pen, picked up the writing pad, and got up.

'I'm going for a walk, Mam,' I said, and went out into the sunshine.

*   *   *

I sat on the bank near the kissing gate and spent a few minutes listening to the sounds of early summer. Then I unscrewed my fountain pen and began to write.

Dear Annabel,

Thank you for your lovely letter. I liked the curly wurly handwriting and all those nice words.

    You went away so suddenly. I'm sorry you cried. I did too, but not in front of anybody. I have been thinking and I've decided I no longer want to be a sailor because it would mean being away from you for long ages and I couldn't bear it. Instead I might be a farmer or a doctor or a jockey or an engine driver or a teacher or a footballer or a vet. King of Wales I can't be because Gareth is older than me and he'd be next in line. Yes perhaps I'll be an actor and take over from Gary Cooper. Well only if you promise to be a film star too. If not I could be one of those men in uniforms who stand outside cinemas and you could be an usherette inside. Or I might become a judge. I hope you have a wonderful time with your parents and yes while you are away I shall come to the kissing gate every day and think about you. Our blackbird is singing its head off as I write. Perhaps every kissing gate has a songbird! I think this one knows what I think about you. He knows that I love you more than anything in the world. Please come back soon. I am yours forever and ever amen.

Geraint (GERUNT)

P.S. I hope Ronnie and Lightning are both well.

After a few days I found myself rising early and waiting at the bedroom window for signs of the postman, ready to dart to the door. Each day that passed without a word from Annabel increased my sense of loss and I went in search of things to do. Indeed, I pleased my mother by helping with the redecorating of the chapel vestry and also by collecting bundles of timber for Bopa Betsi's bakehouse oven. Betsi was the only one still using the old system of baking bread and did so on a communal scale, with many families contributing quantities of the wartime grade flour that so far had not been rationed. So meticulous was Betsi that she would insist on having only ash wood for her big oven. Anyone foolish enough to bring her beech or birch or elm would be sent back to the forest. After heating the cavity with burning logs she would replace the embers with shaped dough loaves before sealing up the oven door with wet clay. The delightful smell of fresh baked bread was usually wonderful enough to take your mind off just about everything. But now it failed to distract me and I decided it was time I finished a commitment that had been on my mind for too long.

I resumed the carving where I had abandoned it on the day of the big freeze. After completing our linked initials I carved a traditional arrow-pierced heart that Michelangelo would have been proud of. Ideally I would have added something to indicate the fact that although Annabel was away from me I still felt her influence. Had I been blessed with the patience and the rest of the day at my disposal I would have carved out one of Bopa Angharad's favourite lines; in fact her second favourite line after 'Let God go with you', namely, *'Er diffodd o'r golau, erys gwres y fflam'*. 'Although the light has been extinguished, the warmth of the flame remains'. Bopa had lost three husbands . . .

A full week went by and I assumed from the absence of any reply to my letter that the return of the Webbs must be imminent.

I thought that it would be a pity if the evacuees were not back in time to hear the announcement of the examination results.

When Eaglebeak walked into the school with his bundle of papers we were all feeling a bit apprehensive.

The headmaster took up his position in front of us and slowly removed his spectacles from their case. He looked different somehow and suddenly I knew why: his cane was missing! When he began to speak he sounded different, too. His tone was untypically soft. Gentle, even.

'Young people,' he said, 'today you are going to have a lesson about life which no school could possibly teach; a lesson that you will not have been properly prepared to receive. What I am going to tell you will shock you and no doubt cause pain and distress. Nevertheless I am compelled to say it.'

My first reaction was that this examination business is more serious than I had thought. Then the feeling of alarm deepened.

My God, why were all the teachers looking so grim? Such pale frowning faces! What the hell was going on? Sensing the gravity of it all, a girl in the front row burst into tears and was gently taken from the hall by Miss Thomas. The headmaster continued:

'Last night many heavy bombs fell in an entirely unexpected raid over south-east England. Although several enemy aircraft were destroyed, a terrible price was paid.'

Please, Mr David, get to the point!

'Several streets in Chatham suffered direct hits and it is my bitter duty to tell you that some of our friends lost their lives. I was called to the police station this morning and had a long telephone conversation with Miss Brownham; who, as you know, went back with the evacuees for their temporary stay. Although she was terribly upset, she was able to tell me the names of those who perished.'

I went rigid and held my breath. I bit my lip and clenched my fists.

Eaglebeak continued, slowly reading out the names and occasionally raising his voice to compete with the sobbing that now filled the hall.

'Albert Blenkinsop . . . Martin Greaves . . .'

Please God, please God, please God, *Please* God.

'. . . and also how especially tragic for a brother and sister to be taken away . . .'

No, God! *No, God! Please!* For *God's sake*, God!

'Ronald Webb and his sister Annabel . . . and their parents . . .'

*   *   *

The sun was still low in the east as I stood at the kissing gate and felt the coldness of the top rail. I looked for the blackbird, but couldn't see or hear him. Everything seemed unusually still; dormant, as if every living creature was lying up, reluctant to face a new day. It seemed as though the same Force that cycles the seasons and causes the moon to trip the tides was somehow on hold.

For several days I had been subdued, taciturn, and remarkably tear-free. Trauma had even made me unable to recall Annabel's face, and I wandered around like a lost soul, sensitive to neither the sympathetic hugs of friends and relatives nor their words of comfort. It was in a state of despair that I had come again to the kissing gate, our trysting place.

However, my torment was now being amplified by a crazy kaleidoscope of recent biography. Images flashed through my brain, but Annabel was not among them: silkworms . . . incendiary bombs . . . Scouts' staves . . . Walter . . . piglets . . . They came and went. Candles . . . cotton reels . . . hand grenades . . .

Eaglebeak . . . Dr Glennie . . . freezing rain . . . Stanislav's letters still fluttering down like snowflakes . . . everything but the image of my lost love.

And then came the flash of Lightning! I saw the old tortoise as he might have been on his last day: solemnly munching his lettuce before withdrawing for the night; the night of the Bomb. I smiled – but was quickly overcome by a bout of uncontrollable grief . . .

But now the iron rail seemed to have warmed in my grasp. The blackbird was singing again, and I fancied I caught a delicate hint of jasmine.

And then! I saw my lost Treasure in all her incomparable beauty, exactly as she had been on that unforgettable day of our last visit to the kissing gate! This time she was holding a posy of exquisitely beautiful flowers of many colours. She was smiling . . . and then she was gone.